Jamie Delano
Grant Morrison
Garth Ennis
**Writers**

David Lloyd
Sean Phillips
Richard Piers Rayner
Mark Buckingham
**Artists**

Lovern Kindzierski
David Lloyd
Tom Ziuko
Matt Hollingsworth
**Colorists**

Todd Klein
Tom Frame
Gaspar Saladino
Elita Fell
Clem Robins
**Letterers**

JOHN CONSTANTINE, HELLBLAZER: RARE CUTS

Dave McKean
David Lloyd
Kent Williams
Glenn Fabry
John Eder
Original Series Covers

Karen Berger — VP-Executive Editor & Editor-original series
Stuart Moore — Editors-original series
Lou Stathis
Axel Alonso
Art Young — Associate Editor-original series
Tom Peyer — Assistant Editor-original series
Jennifer Lee
Scott Nybakken — Editor-collected edition
Robbin Brosterman — Senior Art Director
Amie Brockway-Metcalf — Art Director
Paul Levitz — President & Publisher
Georg Brewer — VP-Design & Retail Product Development
Richard Bruning — Senior VP-Creative Director
Patrick Caldon — Senior VP-Finance & Operations
Chris Caramalis — VP-Finance
Terri Cunningham — VP-Managing Editor
Alison Gill — VP-Manufacturing
Rich Johnson — VP-Book Trade Sales
Hank Kanalz — VP-General Manager, WildStorm
Lillian Laserson — Senior VP & General Counsel
Jim Lee — Editorial Director-WildStorm
David McKillips — VP-Advertising & Custom Publishing
John Nee — VP-Business Development
Gregory Noveck — Senior VP-Creative Affairs
Cheryl Rubin — Senior VP-Brand Management
Bob Wayne — VP-Sales & Marketing

JOHN CONSTANTINE, HELLBLAZER: RARE CUTS

DC Comics, 1700 Broadway, New York, NY 10019
A Warner Bros. Entertainment Company
Printed in Canada. First Printing.
ISBN: 1-4012-0240-3

Cover illustration by Tim Bradstreet

# TABLE OF CONTENTS

Newcastle: A Taste of
Things to Come   From HELLBLAZER #11 ...................... 4
Written by Jamie Delano • Art by Richard Piers Rayner
and Mark Buckingham
Coloring by Lovern Kindzierski • Lettering by Todd Klein

Early Warning   From HELLBLAZER #25 ...................... 31
Written by Grant Morrison • Art and color by David Lloyd
Lettering by Tom Frame

How I Learned to Love
the Bomb   From HELLBLAZER #26 ...................... 56
Written by Grant Morrison • Art and color by David Lloyd
Lettering by Tom Frame

Dead-Boy's Heart   From HELLBLAZER #35 ...................... 81
Written by Jamie Delano • Art by Sean Phillips
Coloring by Tom Ziuko • Lettering by Gaspar Saladino

This Is the Diary of
Danny Drake   From HELLBLAZER #56 ......................106
Written by Garth Ennis • Art and color by David Lloyd
Lettering by Elita Fell

In Another Part of Hell   From HELLBLAZER #84 ......................131
Written by Jamie Delano • Art by Sean Phillips
Coloring by Matt Hollingsworth • Lettering by Clem Robins

Years Gone By:
A HELLBLAZER Timeline   Written by Michael Bonner ......................156

John Constantine's London   Written by Michael Bonner ......................158

JOHN CONSTANTINE
HELLBLAZER

NO. 11 NOV 88
US $1.25
CAN $1.75 UK 70p
NEW FORMAT

SUGGESTED FOR
MATURE READERS

NEWCASTLE

Jamie Delano
Richard Piers Rayner
Mark Buckingham

MEMORIES ARE ALL THAT'S LEFT--AND THESE COLD, RUINED BODIES LAID OUT TO ROT, WITHERING IN THE SEEPING ACID RAIN--

--GAUNT, RUSTED MEMORIALS TO THOSE POISONED HERE AND DEAD AROUND THE WORLD, NOW BURIED IN THE DECADE.

IN THOSE DAYS WE WERE YOUNG--NOT INNOCENT BUT FREE.

EXCITED, STRONG, THE WORLD WAS OURS TO SHAPE ACCORDING TO OUR WILL.

BUT THAT WAS THEN.

BEFORE THATCHER. BEFORE THE FALKLANDS WAR. BEFORE THE COUNTRY--STARVING-- ATE OUT ITS OWN HEART.

BEFORE HELL IMPALED AND TOASTED US, WRITHING OVER THE ROARING FIRES OF OUR OWN INADEQUACIES.

THEN WE WERE A TEAM.

FRANK, ON HOLIDAY FROM TROUBLE IN CALIFORNIA, AND JUDITH, WHO I MET AT THE NORTH BEACH ASHRAM, STUDYING TANTRIC YOGA.

ANNE-MARIE, THE LONELY PSYCHIC; FAT, FORTY, AND SECRETLY IN LOVE WITH ME.

RITCHIE SIMPSON-- COMPUTER FREAK, DEADHEAD AND QUANTUM MAGIC PIONEER.

GARY LESTER--MUSICIAN, COUNTER-CULTURE CLONE AND SMALL-TIME CONJURER.

BENJAMIN, THE SPOOKY TWELVE-YEAR-OLD GENIUS AND ENCYCLO-PEDIA OF ARCANA--

--AND ME.

AND OH-- ♪ WE ♪ COULD BE HEROES, ♫ JUST FOR ONE ♪ DAY. ♫

6

NEWCASTLE, EH? WHAT A *CRUD PIT*. REMINDS ME OF *PITTSBURGH*.

SO THIS IS WHERE *MUCOUS MEMBRANE* MADE THEIR DEBUT. NOT EXACTLY THE *FILLMORE*, IS IT?

AND *WE* AIN'T THE *GRATEFUL DEAD*, NEITHER. WE'RE *NEW WAVE*--AIN'T WE, JOHN?

SURE, GAZ, YEAH.

IT'S ALL LOCKED UP. BETTER KICK IT IN OR WE'LL DROWN IN THIS POXY RAIN. IF LOGUE'S IN THERE, WE'LL JUST SAY WE'VE COME FOR THE *DOOR MONEY* HE SCREWED US OUT OF.

EVERYONE WHO MOVED IN OCCULT CIRCLES KNEW ALEX LOGUE AS A CRAP-HEAD OF THE FIRST ORDER-- A SEX AND DRUGS MAGICIAN-- BUT HE HAD THIS CLUB, AND WE'D NEEDED A GIG FOR THE BAND.

OKAY, WHO WANTS A *DRINK?*

K-CHANGG!

AFTER THE SET, HE'D INVITED US DOWN TO HIS "CHAPEL" TO GET SMASHED AND DO SOME "MAGIC" WITH SIX NYMPHETTES AND A BUNCH OF SEEDY HIPPIES.

PHTOO! IT'S *ROTTEN*.

LESTER WAS INTO IT--AND *I* WAS TEMPTED, UNTIL I SAW HIS LITTLE DAUGHTER, ASTRA, AND THE WAY HE STROKED HER WHILE SHE SAT ON HIS FAT KNEE, STARING LIKE A WHITE-FACED DOLL.

SOMETHING *AWFUL* HAPPENED HERE.

SO WHEN RAY MONDE STARTED TO GET REPORTS OF DISTURBANCES AND PHENOMENA IN NEWCASTLE, *THIS* SEEMED THE OBVIOUS PLACE TO LOOK.

JOHN, THERE'S A CELLAR DOOR--

I KNOW, BEN.

--AND I HEARD *SOUNDS* BEHIND IT.

7

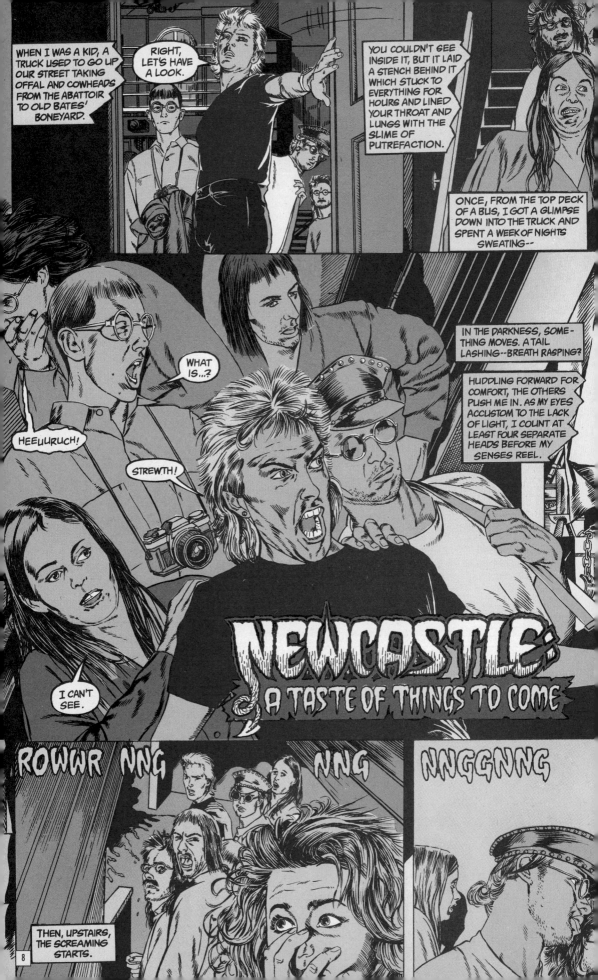

WHEN I WAS A KID, A TRUCK USED TO GO UP OUR STREET TAKING OFFAL AND COWHEADS FROM THE ABATTOIR TO OLD BATES' BONEYARD.

RIGHT, LET'S HAVE A LOOK.

YOU COULDN'T SEE INSIDE IT, BUT IT LAID A STENCH BEHIND IT WHICH STUCK TO EVERYTHING FOR HOURS AND LINED YOUR THROAT AND LUNGS WITH THE SLIME OF PUTREFACTION.

ONCE, FROM THE TOP DECK OF A BUS, I GOT A GLIMPSE DOWN INTO THE TRUCK AND SPENT A WEEK OF NIGHTS SWEATING--

WHAT IS...?

HEEUURUCH!

STREWTH!

IN THE DARKNESS, SOME-THING MOVES. A TAIL LASHING--BREATH RASPING?

HUDDLING FORWARD FOR COMFORT, THE OTHERS PUSH ME IN. AS MY EYES ACCUSTOM TO THE LACK OF LIGHT, I COUNT AT LEAST FOUR SEPARATE HEADS BEFORE MY SENSES REEL.

I CAN'T SEE.

# NEWCASTLE: A TASTE OF THINGS TO COME

ROWWR NNG   NNG   NNGGNNG

THEN, UPSTAIRS, THE SCREAMING STARTS.

--IMAGINING HOW IT WOULD BE TO FALL INTO THAT MESS OF SPLINTERED BONE, TORN FLESH AND EYELESS SKULLS-- WALLOWING, CHOKING IN THE BLOOD AND BILE AND MAGGOTS.

THE SCENT OF *CARNAGE* IS UNFORGETTABLE. ACRID, RAW--A SCENT YOU CAN *CHEW*.

EEAAAIII NOOO

RAAH ROFF

GROCH

TWO CHOICES. EITHER FACE THE MAYHEM UP ABOVE-- OR STAY HERE IN THE *ABATTOIR*.

NO CONTEST.

9

NO PLEASE GOD GROONCH RRIP NOOOO AAHEEIAIA

HNH HNH HNH YEAARGH GROLF ROFF SCHCRICT AAH

OH NO, D'YA THINK SHE SAW-- Y'KNOW, DOWN THERE.

YEAH, AND HEARD IT.

SKROMMP YEURGHH GROMCH GRRA BING

JESUS, IT'S THE LITTLE KID--LOGUE'S DAUGHTER, ASTRA.

RITCHIE, KILL THAT BLOODY ROW, WILL YOU?

HELLO.

WH- WHAT DO YOU WANT?

TAKE IT EASY, SWEETHEART. DON'T BE FRIGHTENED.

DON'T TOUCH ME! I WON'T DO IT ANYMORE, I DON'T LIKE IT!

WE'RE HERE TO HELP YOU, LUVVY.

OK, IT'S OK. IT'S ME -- JOHN--AND GARY, FROM THE BAND. YOU REMEMBER?

13

LIKE AN INTERN, CALLED EARLY TO PERFORM THE *SURGEON'S* ART, I UNPACK MY BAG OF TRICKS WITH NERVOUS HAND.

THIS REALLY TURNS YOU *ON*, DOESN'T IT?

I WOULDN'T DO IT IF IT *DIDN'T*.

HERE, GET THIS ON.

WHAT YOU SAID TO FRANK--ABOUT BLOWING UP IF ANYTHING GOES *WRONG*...?

THAT WAS JUST TO KEEP *HIM* OUT OF MISCHIEF.

NOTHING CAN GO WRONG-- I *PROMISE*.

SO WE'RE REALLY GOING TO CONJURE A *DEMON* FROM *HELL*?

DON'T SEE WHY *NOT*. SEEMS TO BE JUST LIKE *COOKING*.

AS LONG AS YOU'VE GOT THE RIGHT *INGREDIENTS* AND FOLLOW THE RECIPE-- *VOILÀ*.

YOU'RE NOT *SCARED*, ARE YOU?

YES, A BIT. BUT I SORT OF LIKE IT-- ESPECIALLY SINCE THAT FREAKY *ANNE-MARIE'S* OUT OF THE WAY WITH THE *KID*.

THE WAY SHE MAKES *SHEEP'S-EYES* AT YOU ALL THE TIME IS *EMBARRASSING*. YOU'RE NOT *MAKING* IT WITH HER, ARE YOU?

WHY? WHAT'S IT TO YOU-- *JEALOUS*?

LOOK, I'VE GOT IT. BASTARD THIN IT'S A *TIGER*, THOUGH--SCRATCH ME ALL OVER.

WHAT? OH YEAH, THE *CAT*. BETTER LE IT GO AGAIN AND GE KITTED UP. I'VE CHANGED MY MIND ABOUT THE SACRIFICE *SORRY*, MATE.

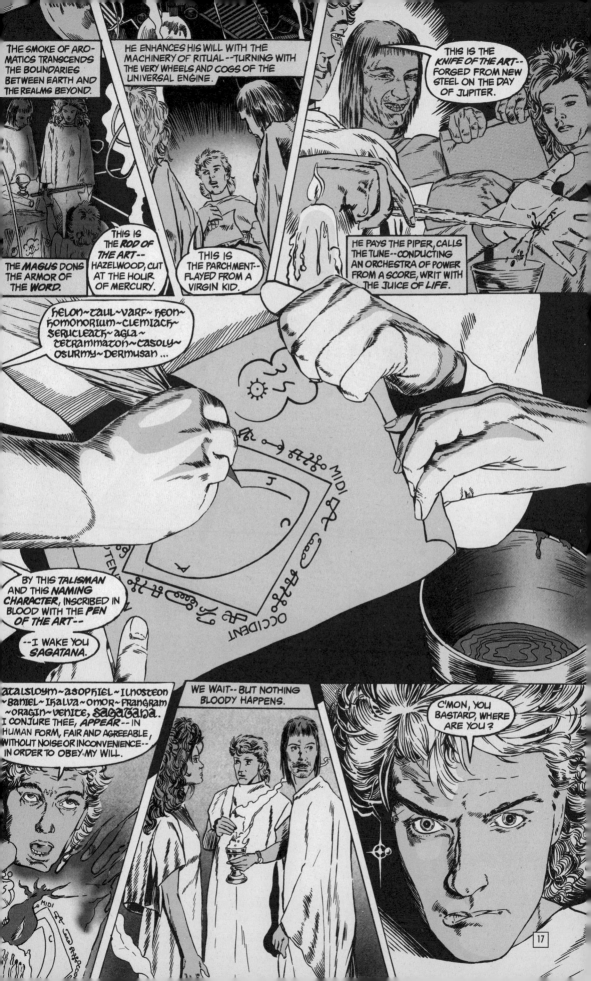

THE SMOKE OF AROMATICS TRANSCENDS THE BOUNDARIES BETWEEN EARTH AND THE REALMS BEYOND.

HE ENHANCES HIS WILL WITH THE MACHINERY OF RITUAL--TURNING WITH THE VERY WHEELS AND COGS OF THE UNIVERSAL ENGINE.

THIS IS THE KNIFE OF THE ART-- FORGED FROM NEW STEEL ON THE DAY OF JUPITER.

THE MAGUS DONS THE ARMOR OF THE WORD.

THIS IS THE ROD OF THE ART-- HAZELWOOD, CUT AT THE HOUR OF MERCURY.

THIS IS THE PARCHMENT-- FLAYED FROM A VIRGIN KID.

HE PAYS THE PIPER, CALLS THE TUNE--CONDUCTING AN ORCHESTRA OF POWER FROM A SCORE, WRIT WITH THE JUICE OF LIFE.

HELON~TAUL~VARF~HEON ~HOMONORIUM~CLEMIALH~ SERUGEATH~AGLA ~ TETRAMMATON~CASOLY~ OSURMY~DERMUSAN ...

BY THIS TALISMAN AND THIS NAMING CHARACTER, INSCRIBED IN BLOOD WITH THE PEN OF THE ART--

--I WAKE YOU SAGATANA.

ATALSLOYM~ASOPHIEL~ILNOSTEON ~BANIEL~IKALVA~OMOR~FRANGRAM ~ORAGIN~VENITE, SAGATANA. I CONJURE THEE, APPEAR--IN HUMAN FORM, FAIR AND AGREEABLE, WITHOUT NOISE OR INCONVENIENCE-- IN ORDER TO OBEY MY WILL.

WE WAIT--BUT NOTHING BLOODY HAPPENS.

C'MON, YOU BASTARD, WHERE ARE YOU?

17

YEAH, GOOD **SHOW**. SHAME ABOUT THE **PUNCHLINE**.

WHAT NOW, JOHN? SHALL I GET ANOTHER **CAT**?

QUIET. SHUT UP. IT'S NOT OVER YET. THE TRICKY BASTARD'S PLAYING HARD TO GET.

YOU'VE GOT TO SHOW THEM WHO'S **BOSS**.

**SAGATANA**, ONCE AGAIN, BY THE POWER OF THE **ART** HERE WROUGHT AROUND YOU--BY THE NAMES OF YOUR LORDS, **LUCIFER, BEELZEBUB, BELIAL** --

ATTEND ME **NOW**--OR BURN FOREVER IN THE **FIRE OF SUNS**.

BUT AGAIN, NOTHING. NOT EVEN THE PATHETIC SPUTTER OF A DAMP SQUIB.

LOOKS LIKE THIS **GRIMORIUM VERUM** RECIPE BOOK THING THAT BENJAMIN SOLD YOU WAS A PIG IN A POKE, THEN.

I CAN'T UNDERSTAND IT. I'VE DONE EVERYTHING BY THE BOOK.

LITTLE SOD. WAIT 'TIL I GET MY HANDS ON HIM. TWO HUNDRED QUID, THAT COST.

DON'T BE **TOO** UPSET. I EXPECT YOU'LL GET TO MEET A REAL DEMON **ONE** DAY.

LOOKS LIKE WE'LL **HAVE** TO LET OLD FREE-WHEELIN' FRANK SHOOT IT, THEN?

YEAH, SO IT SEEMS.

18

BUT...?

SO WHY DID YOU *COME*, CHUM?

BECAUSE IT GREATLY *PLEASURES* ME, TO CHASTEN *ARROGANCE* AND CORRODE THE BRASS OF *VANITY.*

IT'S WITH THE WITLESS OF YOUR SORT THAT *HELL* ENJOYS ITS FINEST *SPORT.*

THE *CHARACTER* YOU DESCRIBED WAS MINE -- BUT *SAGATANA'S* NOT THE *NAME* THAT FITS. AND THUS YOUR INVOCATION LACKED THE WEIGHT OF MAGICAL IMPERATIVE.

AND NOW--SINCE I HAVE *FREELY* PRANCED AND DANCED ACCORDING TO YOUR *FUTILE* ART-- JUSTICE DECREES THAT I SHOULD CLAIM MY *FEE.*

I'LL TAKE THIS CHILD OF TORTURED HEART, TO EASE ME THROUGH ETERNITY.

*NO! I* SCREWED IT UP. TAKE *ME* IF YOU MUST.

*YOU?* NO, *YOU* ARE MINE ALREADY-- AND YOUR FRIENDS. FRESH BLOOMS TO BE ANTICIPATED, PLUCKED ACCORDING TO MY *WHIM.*

I WANT *HER* NOW. THERE IS NO NEGOTIATION--ALTHOUGH AS A SPECIAL DISPENSATION-- IF YOU *INSIST,* I GIVE YOU LEAVE, *ACCOMPANY* HER BELOW.

"STEP FORWARD, *HERO* -- IF YOU WOULD CONQUER FEAR -- AND FULLY COMPREHEND THE MEANING OF THE WORDS, *ABANDON HOPE ALL YE WHO ENTER HERE.*"

CATASTROPHE, FROM START TO FINISH. INEXCUSABLE, STUPID, BLOODY SHAMEFUL *CATASTROPHE*.

NO ONE TO BLAME. I HOLD THE SMOKING GUN--THE ACCUSATORY FINGERS POINT *MY* WAY.

STILL, WE *ALL* MAKE MISTAKES-- DON'T WE? EVEN *DEMONS*. THE ONLY DIFFERENCE IS, *I'VE* PAID FOR *MINE*.

TWO YEARS IN *RAVENSCAR* SECURE FACILITY FOR THE *DANGEROUSLY DERANGED*.

WE *ALL* PAID.

ANNE-MARIE TOOK HOLY ORDERS. BENJAMIN GOT HIS STUTTER. LESTER GOT HIS JUNK HABIT.

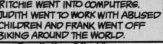

RITCHIE WENT INTO COMPUTERS. JUDITH WENT TO WORK WITH ABUSED CHILDREN AND FRANK WENT OFF BIKING AROUND THE WORLD.

AND, JUST AS THE DEMON PROMISED, HELL TOOK THEM, EVERY ONE.

BUT, LIKE I SAY, WE ALL MAKE MISTAKES --AND THE DEMON'S WAS FINALLY TELLING ME HIS *NAME*.

*NERGAL*.

NERGAL.

THIS IS WHERE WE STARTED IT AND THIS IS WHERE IT'LL *FINISH*.

THIS IS THE KILLING- GROUND WHERE I TAKE MY *REVENGE* -- JUST AS SOON AS I WORK OUT EXACTLY *HOW*.

IT'S A FUNNY THING. I'VE ONLY JUST REALIZED THAT *CASANOVA MEANS NEWCASTLE*. PERHAPS THAT'S WHAT THE FORTUNE-TELLER ON CLACTON PIER MEANT WHEN SHE SAID "PHILANDERING" WOULD BE MY DOWNFALL.

OH WELL-- WE'LL SEE.

*End*

AYE. RIGHT ENOUGH.

SO, EH... WHAT LINE OF BUSINESS YOU IN?

YOU KNOW. THIS AND THAT.

WHEELING AND DEALING.

SAY NO MORE, PAL. SAY NO MORE.

THATCHER'S BRITAIN, EH? WE ALL GET BY AS BEST WE CAN.

WELL, THIS IS YOUR STOP, PAL. THURSDYKE'S ABOUT TWO MILES UP THAT SIDE ROAD.

THAT'S WHERE THEY'RE HAVING THIS BIG PARADE, AM I RIGHT? SAW IT ON THE NEWS.

THAT'S THE PLACE.

ANYWAY, NICE TALKING TO YOU, PAL.

YEAH. YOU TOO, MATE. THANKS FOR THE LIFT.

TAKE CARE.

HOPE YOU GET THE WEATHER FOR YOUR PARADE BUT I DON'T LIKE THE LOOK OF THAT SKY.

COULD BE A STORM ON THE WAY.

JESUS CHRIST! JOHN!

DO YOU **HAVE** TO DO THAT?

'LO LOVE. NICE TO SEE YOU AGAIN.

DO **WHAT** ANYWAY?

CHRIST, YOU KNOW! POP UP OUT OF **NOWHERE** ALL THE TIME.

YEAH, WELL, THAT'S **ME**, ENNIT?

ENIGMATIC.

SO I TAKE IT YOU GOT MY **MESSAGE** THEN?

I THOUGHT YOU MIGHT **ENJOY** THIS CARNIVAL THING. A BIT OF THE OLD **PAGAN** STUFF.

IT'S A QUEER OLD DUMP THIS, ENNIT?

THERE'S AN ATMOSPHERE LIKE WAITING FOR A **FUNERAL**.

I THOUGHT YOU MIGHT NOT COME. TOO MANY BAD MEMORIES.

WE'RE ONLY ABOUT TWENTY MILES FROM **RAVENSCAR** HERE.

THOSE WERE THE DAYS. TWITCHING AND DROOLING IN THE **ECT** ROOM.

YOU STILL HEARING THE **VOICES**, THEN?

ONLY WHEN I STOP TAKING THE TABLETS.

THAT GROUP IN **LEEDS** THAT YOU PUT ME ON TO — THEY REALLY OPENED MY EYES...

UNA, LISTEN... I DON'T SUPPOSE YOU COULD LEND US A COUPLE OF QUID FOR A PACKET OF FAGS...?

ONLY I FINISHED MY LAST ONE AND I'M **GASPING**.

I'LL PAY YOU BACK.

HONEST.

...SO I MANAGED TO PERSUADE MY **MAGAZINE** TO PAY THE TRAIN FARE.

THIS FESTIVAL USED TO BE A **MAJOR** EVENT BUT IT DIED OUT EARLY IN THE LAST CENTURY.

SO WHAT KIND OF FESTIVAL ARE WE TALKING ABOUT?

TWENTY SILK CUT, LOVE, AND A BOX OF...

BLOODY HELL!

YOU JUST ABOUT SHAT A BRICK THEN, EH?

JESUS.

IT'S **THAT** KIND OF FESTIVAL.

BANG GOES YOUR STREET CRED, JOHN.

THE SOIL VIBRATES.

JOHN GOSS, WALKING HOME FROM THE SHEEP, CAN FEEL IT IN THE SOLES OF HIS FEET.

SUBTLE TREMORS, LIKE A BELLSTROKE UNDERGROUND.

AND A NOTE THAT CANNOT BE HEARD RINGS UP THROUGH THE TREE.

THE TREE LIKE A TUNING-FORK AND THE BIRDS RISING IN A FEATHERED CLOUD.

EACH ONE CARRIES THE NOTE. EACH BIRD REPEATS IT ON THE AUDIBLE SCALE.

THEY SAY THAT IF ALL THE CROWS IN A WOOD FORSAKE IT SUDDENLY, IT IS SURELY A WARNING OF DISASTER.

OLD WIVES' TALES.

SUPERSTITION.

...I MEAN, WE'RE TALKING ABOUT A COMMUNITY ON ITS **KNEES** HERE, JOHN.

WHEN THE GOVERNMENT CLOSED THE **PITS**, IT KICKED THE GUTS OUT OF THURSDYKE.

THAT'S WHAT THIS WHOLE **CARNIVAL** THING'S ABOUT— AN ATTEMPT TO SALVAGE SOME COMMUNITY SPIRIT. TO SHOUT *"WE'RE NOT DEAD!"* TO THE WORLD...

JOHN...?

JOHN, ARE YOU ALL RIGHT?

SORRY, UNA...

SOMEONE JUST WALKED OVER MY **GRAVE**.

GO ON WITH WHAT YOU WERE SAYING...

WHY DON'T YOU ALL PISS OFF!

I DON'T BLAME THEM. THIS COUNTRY'S TURNING INTO AN **AIRCRAFT CARRIER** FOR THE BLOODY YANKS.

YOU SHOULD TALK TO THE **PARSON** HERE, JOHN. HIS NAME'S **BAYLISS**.

HE'S AN EX-RAF PILOT WHO'S BEEN AN ANTI-NUCLEAR **ACTIVIST** SINCE THE EARLY '60'S.

...SO WHAT WAS ALL **THAT** ABOUT, BACK AT THE PUB?

OH, IT'S THIS **MISSILE BASE** UP ON THE MOOR. IT'S TO BE EXPANDED AND IT'S BRINGING **WORK** INTO THE AREA BUT THE **CND** PEOPLE ARE UP IN ARMS.

SO WHEN DO THE **FESTIVITIES** START?

FOUR O'CLOCK TOMORROW MORNING, BY THE WAR MEMORIAL. THERE'LL BE QUITE A BIT OF **MEDIA** COVERAGE TOO.

I THINK THAT'S WHY THE **PROTESTORS** HAVE CHOSEN TO...

JOHN?

WHAT'S UP?

IS SOMETHING **WRONG**?

NO. NOTHING'S WRONG.

I THOUGHT I **SAW** SOMETHING...

I DON'T KNOW. THERE'S SOMETHING **FUNNY** ABOUT THIS PLACE.

**YOU'RE** PSYCHIC. CAN'T YOU **FEEL** ANYTHING?

LIKE I SAID: ONLY WHEN I STOP TAKING THE **TABLETS**.

IT'S A NICE LITTLE CHURCH THOUGH.

HAVE YOU SEEN **THIS**?

AREN'T THEY **BRILLIANT**? I **LOVE** THESE OLD CARVINGS.

I MEAN, THAT'S GOT TO BE A **PRE-CHRISTIAN** IMAGE.

YEAH. THEY CALL IT THE **MAW**.

IT'S SUPPOSED TO REPRESENT THE OPENING INTO THE **UNDERWORLD**.

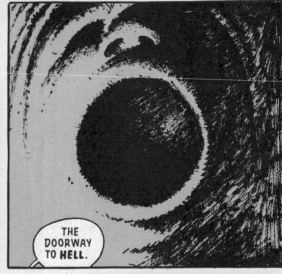

THE DOORWAY TO **HELL**.

AH!

ADMIRING OUR FAMOUS **CARVINGS**, I SEE.

**GODFREY BAYLISS**. PLEASED TO MEET YOU.

AND WELCOME TO **THURSDYKE**.

...OBVIOUSLY I CANNOT ENTIRELY **APPROVE** OF A REVIVED PAGAN CELEBRATION BUT ANYTHING *THAT* SERVES TO UNITE OUR COMMUNITY CAN HARDLY BE **CONDEMNED**.

IT'S THE WAY IN WHICH WE HAVE SOMEHOW... SOLD THE **SOUL** OF THURSDYKE, SHALL WE SAY?

THIS EXTENSION OF THE MISSILE BASE.

WELL, IT'S JOBS, ENNIT?

WHEN YOU HAVEN'T ANY MONEY, IT'S EASY TO SWAP A **DAVY LAMP** FOR A **CONTAMINATION SUIT.**

AH YES, **JOBS**. ONCE UPON A TIME, SOULS WERE TRADED FOR **IMMORTALITY** OR **RICHES**. NOW WE ARE BOUGHT AND SOLD WITH THE PROMISE OF **JOBS.**

THE HUMAN SPIRIT IS DEVALUED CURRENCY. HOW THE **DEVIL** MUST BE LAUGHING.

AND IT'S NOT ONLY THE MISSILE BASE. SOMETIMES THE CHURCH BELLS RING IN SYMPATHY WITH... **VIBRATIONS** UNDERGROUND.

THE MOORS ARE RIDDLED WITH VAULTS AND TUNNELS. MINISTRY OF DEFENSE PROPERTY. ELECTRIC FENCES AND WAR DOGS...

WHO KNOWS WHAT NEW AND TERRIBLE WEAPONS ARE BEING IMAGINED DOWN THERE?

THIS SOIL IS SICK WITH SECRETS, MR. CONSTANTINE.

AND I FEAR FOR THE FUTURE.

AHH

GOD HAS
DESERTED US,
MR. CONSTANTINE.

TONIGHT WE SHALL SEE IF THE **OLD** GODS HAVE ANYTHING **BETTER** TO OFFER.

A DOOR SLAMS.

DEEP IN THE EARTH, A DOOR SLAMS.

THE ROOM RINGS LIKE A WINE GLASS.

THE ELECTRIC CLOCK HAS STOPPED.

OUTSIDE THE NOISE GETS LOUDER.

TIN DRUMS.

PICCOLOS.

BAD DREAM MUSIC.

AND THE LIGHTS ARE FEVER-LIGHTS, LIKE THE GHOSTS OF FIREWORKS.

FIREWORKS WALKING.

THE WINDOWPANE SHIVERS.

THE PARADE GOES BY.

THE WHOLE ROOM HUMS LIKE A BELL.

...CHRIST HAS COME DOWN FROM THE CROSS. THE HAUNTED CROSS. WE ARE FORSAKEN...

FATHER, A SIGN.

GIVE ME A SIGN!

OH LIGHT! SUCH A LIGHT!

GHOSTS OF GLASS!

SET FREE!

THE SAINTS HAVE LEFT THE GLASS AND FILLED ME WITH LIGHT.

I AM A BOTTLE. CORKED AND FILLED WITH SPIRIT-LIGHT.

"ASK, AND IT SHALL BE GIVEN YOU; SEEK AND YE SHALL FIND;

" KNOCK, AND IT SHALL BE OPENED UNTO YOU. "

HOW DOES IT BEGIN? IT BEGINS WITH THE SOUND OF BREAKING GLASS.

SOMEWHERE, A CHILD CRIES AND CRIES AND CRIES.

AND STOPS.

ABRUPTLY.

DAD AND MICHAEL COME IN THE NIGHT TO SLEEPING RACHEL ACKROYD.

SOLICITOUS DAD TAKES HER ASIDE AND TEACHES HER THE FACTS OF LIFE.

MR. BONE THE BUTCHER GRUNTS AND SNUFFLES AND WHETS HIS RAZORS.

WHILE PINNED TO A SLAB OF MARBLE, DREAMING OF MAKEUP AND MINI-SKIRTS, BILLY BEGS FOR CASTRATION.

AND SOMEONE COUNTS TO TEN.

AND THE PARADE GOES BY.

NURSERY RHYMES. SCREAMS OF ECSTASY AND OF PAIN. BROADCASTS ON INAUDIBLE FREQUENCIES. DISSONANT MUSIC. A GREAT ORCHESTRAL SWELL OF NOISE.

IT IS THE MUSIC OF TRANSFIGURATION.

FIN HOTEL

AND THE DEVIL, AS ALWAYS, HAS THE BEST TUNES.

I DID IT.

I **DID** IT. SOMEHOW I JUST COULDN'T STOP MYSELF.

I **HAD** TO DO IT. TO **TEST** THE EQUIPMENT.

MY GOD.

I BOMBARDED THE TOWN WITH **MICROWAVES** SET TO RESONATE WITH THE **TEN Hz** FREQUENCY OF THE HUMAN BRAIN.

ALL THOSE UNCONSCIOUS DESIRES AND FEARS AND REPRESSED LONGINGS. SET **FREE.**

I'VE WOKEN THE SLEEPING GIANT.

WHAT HAVE I DONE, POOLE?

WHAT **HAVE** I DONE?

52

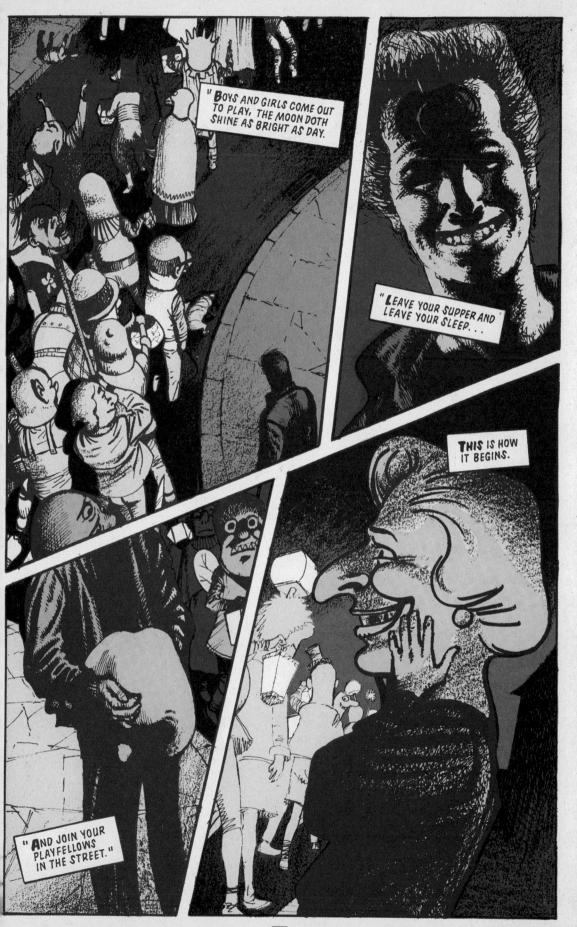

JOHN CONSTANTINE

# HELLBLAZER

NO. 26 FEB 90
US $1.50
CAN $1.85 UK 80p
NEW FORMAT

SUGGESTED FOR
MATURE READERS

Grant Morrison
David Lloyd

THEY HELD HIM DOWN.

THEY STRIPPED HIM AND ANNOINTED HIM.

Filled with complex light.

Dreaming of the glass Jesus. The image filled with holy water.

AND THEY RAISED HIM UP AND DRESSED HIM IN HIS ROBES OF OFFICE.

The Messiah in the form of pure mathematical light.

Captive light. Rain bottled in the image of Jesus.

AND PAINTED HIS FACE.

"Break the glass", the Savior howled.

AND WHISPERED HIS NAME IN REVERENT TONES.

"Break the glass", the Savior howled.

"ARCHBISHOP."

"ARCHBISHOP BOMB."

"ARCHBISHOP BOMB."

57

SOUNDING THE HOURS OF A RESTLESS NIGHT.

PROFESSOR HORROBIN?

I'M NOT SURE I UNDERSTAND WHAT YOU'RE SAYING. WHAT HAVE YOU **DONE**?

PROFESSOR?

A GIANT SLEEPS IN ALL OF US. A BURIED KING. THE BIBLE ASKS, "CANST THOU LOOSE THE BANDS OF ORION?" THIS I HAVE DONE.

I HAVE UNCHAINED PROMETHEUS. WOKEN THE GOD WITHIN...

YOU PEOPLE FROM THE MINISTRY...YOU DON'T UNDERSTAND **ANYTHING**. "WE MUST MAKE CUTS," YOU SAY. "TAKE AWAY HIS FUNDING."

WHAT?

ARE YOU SURE YOU'RE FEELING ALL RIGHT, PROFESSOR?

I MEAN, WELL... THIS **MACHINE** OF YOURS...

AND, BUZZING LIKE INSECTS, THE **KING'S HEAD DARTS TEAM** FEEDS ON THE WINES AND NECTARS OF A DEAD DOG'S BODY.

MR FINN, THE FISHMONGER, IS PULLING THE WINGS OFF BIRDS IN THE PET SHOP.

CANARIES. PARROTS. COCKATIELS.

IN CROMWELL STREET, THE CHILDREN ARE LED SMILING TO THE RAZOR-MAN WHO GENTLY REMOVES THEIR FACES TO MAKE CHILD-MASKS FOR THE ADULTS.

WHEN HE HAS **ENOUGH**, WHEN HE HAS DIVINED THE SECRET OF **FLIGHT**, HE WILL JUMP FROM THE ROOF OF THE TOWN HALL.

THE CHILDREN DEPART, WITH WET RED HALLOWEEN CAKE FACES, SMILING STILL.

AND ALL THE SOUNDS-- OF PAIN, OF GLASS CRUSHED UNDERFOOT-- BECOME ONE GREAT SOUND, LIKE THE DRAWN-OUT FINAL CHIME OF SOME MONUMENTAL BELL, SIGNALING DOOMSDAY.

THE DEVIL HAS COME TO THURSDYKE!

AND THE HOLLOW TOWN HUMS LIKE A HIVE.

67

THE OLD GODS WEAR NEW FACES. THEY DRESS IN NEW CLOTHES THAT THEY MAY WALK AMONG US UNSEEN.

"BEEP BEEP MEANS THE VAN IS COMING... BANG BANG MEANS THE MAN IS DEAD... VROOM VROOM MEANS THE ENGINE'S RUNNING."

AZRAEL. DEATH GOD. DEATH ANGEL.

I RECOGNIZE YOU.

BUT UNDERNEATH THE MASK, THE FACE IS ALWAYS THE SAME.

I KNOW YOU.

SHIT.

WHY...AM I...HERE?

AM I DREAMING? DID I...WAKE?

CHRIST...LEAKS AWAY...DOWN INTO DARKNESS... FALLING...

NO. NOT... DARKNESS. **LIGHT**...SUCH A LIGHT...

NEARER... MY GOD TO... THEE...

NOOO

WE MINED HERE ONCE. COAL. QUARRYING LIGHT FROM THE DARKNESS.

NOW **YOU** BECOME LIGHT. AN OFFERING TO THE GOD OF DAWN.

BURNING IN THE FLOWERY DEATH-CAR.

SOON IT'LL BE **DAWN**, WHEN ALL THE MASKS ARE CAST ASIDE AND WE STAND NAKED BEFORE THE COMING GOD!

JOHN! WHERE ARE YOU, JOHN?

THEY'RE GOING TO BURN ME, JOHN!

LOOK!

HE'S COMING! THREE **STARS** IN THE SKY! STARS OF WARNING!

HE'S COMING!

NOT YET. NOT YET.

THE SKY BECOMES PAPER-THIN. DAWN LIGHT IN A PAPER LANTERN.

THE GOD IS COMING IN A THUNDER OF WINGS.

THE GOD OF THE EAST WITH FACE UNVEILED.

I KNOW YOU.

THE TRAGEDY OF WHAT HAS HAPPENED HERE IN THURSDYKE CANNOT BE UNDERESTIMATED.

AS EMERGENCY SERVICES WORK TO CLEAR THE WRECKAGE, NO CLEAR PICTURE HAS YET EMERGED AS TO THE FINAL DEATH TOLL.

THAT THE TRAGEDY SHOULD OCCUR DURING A FESTIVAL OF CIVIC REGENERATION MAKES IT ALL THE MORE HORRIFIC.

THE PRIME MINISTER, WHO HEARD THE NEWS EARLY THIS MORNING IS CURRENTLY ON HER WAY TO THURSDYKE TO OFFER HER SYMPATHY AND SUPPORT.

POLICE HAVE ALREADY REVEALED THAT A RADICAL ANTI-NUCLEAR GROUP MAY HAVE BEEN RESPONSIBLE FOR THE...

YEAH, THAT'S RIGHT, MATE. FEED THEM ALL THE OLD LIES.

YOU'VE GOT A POSH ACCENT, SO IT **MUST** BE TRUE.

WHAT?

CUT. CUT AND START AGAIN.

BLOODY PAIN IN THE ARSE...

"Do you believe a town can commit suicide?"

SHE SAID.

The town was never alive.

It died years ago and what we have seen was no more than a haunting.

An unquiet spirit tricked out in living colors.

Those lights, those voices: echoes at a seance.

A painted sheet drawn over a corpse.

A mask.

And now the mask is cast away.

BOLLOCKS.

HELLBLAZER 35
US $1.50
$1.85 UK 80p
NOVEMBER 1990

SUGGESTED FOR
MATURE READERS

# JOHN CONSTANTINE
# HELLBLAZER™

JAMIE DELANO • SEAN PHILLIPS

YEAH, DEAD, LIKE MAM--ALL MOLDY AND ROTTEN. OH NO I WON'T. I'M GOING TO BE A *LOST BOY* AND LIVE IN *NEVER NEVER LAND.*

A SHILLING AND *TWO MARS BARS--* OR A SMACKED HEAD.

ALL RIGHT, BUT YOU'LL BE SORRY IF I GET EAT BY THE *BOGEYMAN* AND NEVER COME BACK.

YOU SILLY SOD. THERE'S NO SUCH THING AS BOGEYMEN.

YES THERE IS. ONE LIVES IN THE QUARRY.

THE ABANDONED QUARRY'S OUT OF BOUNDS-- GET CAUGHT AND IT'S A CERTAIN BELTING-- BUT IT'S THE ONLY INTERESTING PLACE IN THIS BORING VILLAGE. OLD MACHINERY'S LIKE ROBOT DINOSAURS GUARDING A FLOODED ENTRANCE TO ANOTHER WORLD.

THE VILLAGE KIDS SAY IT'S BOTTOMLESS-- FULL OF IRON SPIKES AND TANGLED WIRE TO DROWN YOU. BUT IF A SMALL KID COULD HOLD HIS BREATH FOR LONG ENOUGH, PERHAPS HE COULD SWIM RIGHT THROUGH TO NEVER-NEVER LAND.

YOU'D HAVE TO GET PAST THE *BOGEYMAN,* THOUGH. HE'S DANGEROUS--THE VILLAGE KIDS RATTLE HIS HUT WITH STONES AND HE GOES CRACKERS. BUT A GOOD TRACKER COULD GET BY. *UNCAS* COULD DO IT.

P OUT
ANGER
WATER

'ERE, WHITEY, GIVE US A FAG Y' WANKER. WHAT SORT Y' GOT?

SHIT. BLACKFOOT WAR-PARTY.

NELSON'S-- WOGGED 'EM OFF ME DAD.

GOT A MATCH?

YEAH, YOUR FACE AN' MY ARSE. HAWHAWHAW.

OI OI, WE GOT A TRES-PASSER.

WHAT'RE YOU DOING 'ERE, Y' LITTLE SCOUSE BASTARD?

NOTHIN'-- AN' I AIN'T A BASTARD.

YES YOU ARE. YOU AIN'T GOT A MUM.

AND 'IS DAD'S LOCKED UP FOR WOGGING SCANTIES OFF A WASHING-LINE.

LIAR. YOUR UNCLE HARRY TOLD OUR DAD IN THE PUB.

I...I WANT TO BE IN YOUR GANG.

HE AIN'T. HE'S AWAY, WORKING--ON...ON ROCKETS AT CAPE CARNIVAL.

WELL, WE DON'T WANT NO MUCKY SCOUSERS HERE.

ANYWAY, YOU AIN'T GOT THE GUTS T' DO WHAT WE DO.

YES I 'AVE.

EVER KILLED A SLIMY EEL WITH Y' TEETH?

EVER TOUCHED A GIRL'S THING?

WONDER WHERE HE GETS THEM ALL FR...'

OI, SCOUSER-- RUN!

TREACHERY.

BETRAYAL.

KANGG! BAMM! KLONGG!

RRAH... WHYDUNTYA FUGGINKIDSLIV MIALOAN

IT'S CAPTAIN DEATH-- NO PITY IN HIS EYES.

CUMBAK'ERE, BOY. I WUNT T' TALK T' YER.

INTO THE BUSHES-- HEART GALLOPING LIKE A HORSE-- RUN!

DARK, MUSTY SMELL. UGH-- SHITS EVERYWHERE UNDER CRUMPLED NUDEY-BOOKS. IS HE STILL COMING..?

GET IN DEEP, COLD, SHINY LAUREL LEAVES'LL HIDE YOU.

C'MON OUT, Y' LITTLE SOD.

I WON'T HURT YER. JUST WANNA SHOW YER A SECRET.

FREEZE. IF HE CAN'T HEAR YOU, HE CAN'T FIND YOU.

HOLD YOUR BREATH. ONLY THE BUZZING OF FLIES AND A DISTANT BLACKBIRD CHIRPING ALARM. HAS HE GIVEN UP, OR IS IT A TRAP? WAIT.

'THOUSAND. HEART-BEAT'S SLOWING DOWN NOW. HOW MANY 'TIL IT'S SAFE TO COME OUT--FIFTEEN HUNDRED? NO, MORE. KEEP COUNTING.

AND THERE'S SOMETHING BURIED HERE, SOME BONE. PERHAPS IT'S A FOSSIL, A DINOSAUR--OR A PILOT, CRASHED IN THE WAR.

CAREFUL, BRUSH THE EARTH AWAY GENTLY. DO IT PROPERLY, LIKE AN ARCHAEOLOGIST-- MAYBE IT'S THE MISSING-LINK.

THERE'S HIPS AND A WHOLE RIB-CAGE, PART OF AN ARM... BUT NO SKULL. LITTLE BIT SMALLER THAN ME.

AH!

IT'S A DEAD-BOY-- DROWNED AND BURIED BY THE BOGEYMAN. JUST LIKE THE VILLAGE KIDS SAID.

SOMETHING GLEAMING DULLY IN HIS CHEST. A STONE-- DIG IT OUT. WAS THIS EARTH FLESH?

BUT A STONE WITH VEINS? LOOK AT THE SHAPE. JESUS-- IT'S A FOSSIL OF A DEAD-BOY'S HEART.

ANOTHER THREE-THOUSAND, SIX-HUNDRED HEART-BEATS. TIME TO ESCAPE NOW. UNCAS THE MOHICAN HAS RECEIVED A WARRIOR'S GIFT.

ITS MAGIC WILL PROTECT HIM FROM THE BOGEYMAN, FROM THE BLACKFEET. COLD WEIGHT BEATING AGAINST CHEST--DEATH RIDING IN POCKET.

MEOOOW!

OW! HOLD ITS BLEDDY LEGS.

WHAT'LL WE DO WITH IT?

TIE ROCKS TO IT AN' THROW IT IN THE WATER.

NAH-- SET FIRE TO ITS TAIL AND LET IT RUN.

GET CAUGHT AND THEY'LL STEAL IT. SKIRT THE PATH, DOWN THROUGH THE BUSHES AGAIN.

SAVAGES EVERYWHERE-- BUT UNCAS IS CUNNING, UNCAS IS...

KEEP STILL, YOU SILLY COW. I CAN'T BLOODY UNDO IT.

OUCH! YOU'RE HURTING ME.

OW... ACH... YOU'RE TOO ROUGH, KEITH!

WHO...? BLIMEY-- IT'S A KID.

PISS OFF, YOU DIRTY LITTLE SOD!

UNCAS IS STRONG. UNCAS IS BRAVE. UNCAS HAS THE DEAD-BOY'S HEART.

L-LEAVE HER ALONE.

WHAT? I'LL PUNCH YER STUPID LITTLE 'EAD!

AHHH, DON'T. HE'S CUTE. HE'S GOING TO RESCUE ME FROM THE NASTY, HAIRY MAN.

LEAVE 'IM, KEITH-- LET 'IM WATCH.

YOU'D LIKE THAT, WOULDN'T YOU, DARLIN'?

GET YOUR LITTLE HEART BEATING, EH?

WELL, I WOULDN'T, Y' DIRTY MARE. I CAN'T DO IT WITH A KID WATCHING ME!

OH... GO ON. I BET YOU COULD.

OI, OI-- LOOK AT THIS, LADS. THE GREAT SCOUSE SCOUT BAWLIN' 'IS EYES OUT.

WHASSA MATTER-- DIDDUMS GET LOST IN THE SPOOKY QUARRY, THEN?

DID THE BOGEYMAN MAKE Y' SHIT Y' PANTS?

LET ME PAST-- TRAITORS!

TRAITORS, EH? THAT'S NOT VERY NICE.

WHASS IN 'IS SHIRT?

IT'S A NUDEY-BOOK. HE GOT ONE.

GIVE US IT.

NO!

NOTHING IN THE WORLD IS FAIR. EVERYONE'S A SHITBAG. MAM'S A SHITBAG FOR BEING DEAD. DAD'S A SHITBAG FOR GOING TO PRISON.

CHERYL'S A SHITBAG FOR SAYING I WENT OUT WITHOUT ASKING-- AND AUNT DOLLY'S A SHITBAG FOR BELIEVING HER. SHITBAGS. SHITBAGS. SHITBAGS.

BODY ACHES WITH BATTLE-WOUNDS. NETTLE-RASH ON LEGS AND ARMS, FAG-BURNS ON CHEST, ARSE ON FIRE FROM BELTING--BUT WARRIORS DON'T MIND PAIN.

AIN'T FAIR, THOUGH. UNCLE HARRY AIN'T GOT THE RIGHT. HE AIN'T OUR DAD. WHO'S HE TO CALL PEOPLE AUNTYCHRIST, OR WHATEVER IT WAS? AND HE LIKED TO HURT--YOU COULD SEE IT IN HIS EYES.

SINNERS MUST SUFFER PUNISH-MENT, HE'D SAID. RETRIBUTION, JUSTICE... ASK YOUR FATHER. IS AUNTY DOLLY A SINNER AS WELL?

NO HARRY, PLEASE...

NOT THAT WAY. NOT TONIGHT...

HER VOICE AND HIS, DEEPER, WHISPER IN THE WALL. THE HEART MAKES IT LOUDER--SLAPPING, A GROAN, A STIFLED GASP.

DON'T LISTEN TO HER CRYING. SNUGGLE INTO SILENCE. POOR AUNT DOLLY. SHE'D BE GOOD TO CUDDLE--SOFT, BIG ARMS WRAPPING ROUND. WARM.

DEAD-BOY'S HEART IN A LIVE-BOY'S HAND. LIFT IT--HEAVY, COLD.

FRIGHTENING. PRECIOUS. IT FEELS--BLACK.

SLIDE IT, HARD AND SMOOTH, TO REST OVER THE BLISTERED SKIN. FEEL IT SOOTHING-- SOAKING UP THE HURT.

AND LIFT IT BACK TO FEEL ITS WEIGHT PRESSING DOWN-- SQUEEZING ME BACKWARDS INTO DULL, BOOMING, UNDER- WATER SLEEP.

LATER, WALKING, FALLING OUT OF A DREAM—A DEAD BOY IN THE WOODS, BURIED UNDER PILES OF TORN-UP DIRTY-BOOKS. STONE WET WITH DRIBBLE, HEART IN MOUTH.

SOUND. TOILET FLUSHING. MAYBE IT'S CHERYL. WHAT IF SHE'S RUNNING AWAY? WON'T STAY HERE ALONE.

QUIET, THOUGH—IT MIGHT BE UNCLE HARRY. IF YOU TRIPPED HIM DOWNSTAIRS AND HE BROKE HIS NECK, WOULD THEY CATCH YOU?

IT'S AUNT DOLLY. WHAT'S SHE DOING? HELP HER. NO, YOU'LL FRIGHTEN HER—SHE'LL BE CROSS.

WHY DOES HE TIE HER UP—TO STOP HER RUNNING AWAY? MAYBE SHE LETS HIM HURT HER, LIKE THEM IN THE WOODS...?

MAYBE THAT'S WHAT YOU'RE SUPPOSED TO DO... MAYBE CHERYL KNOWS... MAYBE...

96

'MORNING, AUNT DOLLY. 'S UNCLE HARRY GONE TO WORK, THEN?

YES, *YOU'RE* THE SLUG-A-BED. YOUR SISTER'S DOING THE SHOPPING AND I'M HALF-WAY THROUGH THE WASHING ALREADY.

THERE'S PORRIDGE-- COLD NOW -- AND JAM ON THE TABLE. EAT IT QUICK, I HAVEN'T GOT TIME FOR YOU UNDER MY FEET TODAY.

AUNT DOLLY... IS IT TRUE OUR DAD'S IN PRISON FOR NICKING LADIES' SMALLS?

WHO TOLD YOU THAT?

ONE OF THE VILLAGE KIDS SAID UNCLE HARRY'D TOLD HIS DAD.

OH *DID* HE?

SOMETIMES YOUR UNCLE HARRY LETS HIS TONGUE RUN AWAY WITH HIM.

SO IT'S TRUE, THEN!

THERE'S SOME THINGS A YOUNG MIND SHOULDN'T TROUBLE OVER.

BUT OUR DAD'S NOT *STUPID.* IF HE WAS GOING TO STEAL SOME-THING, IT'D BE MORE VALUABLE THAN OLD KNICKERS.

MEN DO SOME STRANGE THINGS IN THIS WORLD, BOY--THINGS ONLY GOD AND THEM UNDERSTAND.

MAYBE YOU'LL SEE CLEARER WHEN YOU GROW UP.

YOU'LL BE ONE OF THEM, THEN-- POOR LITTLE SOD!

I WON'T. I'M NOT GOING TO GROW UP. I'M GOING TO STAY HERE-- WITH YOU!

YOU'RE A FUNNY KID-- YOUR FATHER'S SON, ALL RIGHT.

WHAT'RE YOU DOING WITH THAT OLD STONE?

IT'S NOT A STONE. IT'S A DEAD-BOY'S HEART. IT'S MAGIC. IF YOU RUB IT ON YOUR BRUISES IT'LL TAKE THE ACHE AWAY-- YOU TRY...

UGH! GET AWAY WITH YOUR GRUBBINESS, YOU NASTY LITTLE TYKE.

ANYWAY, I HAVEN'T GOT ANY BRUISES.

I'M OFF OUT TO DO THE CHURCH FLOWERS NOW. YOUR SISTER'LL BE BACK SOON TO HANG THE WASHING OUT.

DON'T GO OUT OF THE GARDEN.

AND GET RID OF THAT DIRTY STONE. IT'LL HAVE DISEASES!

HOW MANY TIMES DID YOUR HEART BEAT BEFORE THE BOGEYMAN CAUGHT YOU, DEAD-BOY?

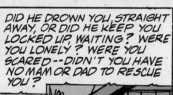

DID HE DROWN YOU, STRAIGHT AWAY, OR DID HE KEEP YOU LOCKED UP, WAITING? WERE YOU LONELY? WERE YOU SCARED--DIDN'T YOU HAVE NO MAM OR DAD TO RESCUE YOU?

AND WHAT WAS THE SECRET THING HE SHOWED YOU? WAS IT DEATH? WAS IT THE WAY TO NEVER-NEVER LAND? IS THAT WHERE YOU ARE NOW? IS IT FUN THERE--IS IT EXCITING?

WHAT'RE YOU DOING, OUR JOHN?

NOTHING. PLAYING.

SORRY I GOT YOU IN TROUBLE YESTERDAY. 'S' UNCLE HARRY, HE FRITS ME-- HE'S SO CREEPY.

'E'S NOT AS BAD AS THE BOGEYMAN.

WHAT'S THIS YOU'RE BUILDING--A CASTLE? LOOKS REALLY GOOD. I'D LIKE TO LIVE THERE.

'S NOT A CASTLE. IT'S A PRISON!

LET'S RUN AWAY BACK TO *LIVERPOOL*, CHERYL. WE COULD HIDE ON THE BOMB-SITES 'TIL THEY LET DAD GO.

IS IT A MAGIC CASTLE, JOHN? WHO LIVES THERE-- PRINCESSES AND MAGICIANS?

URR! WHAT'S THAT MOVING?

I *TOLD* YOU. IT'S A PRISON FOR *INSECTS*. THAT'S THE FLIES-- THEY'RE LOCKED UP FOR SICKING ON PEOPLE'S FOOD.

HERE'S THE LADYBIRDS, FOR GOING OUT AND LEAVING THEIR KIDS TO DIE IN A BURN-ING HOUSE. AND WORMS-- 'COS THEY EAT *DEAD* PEOPLE.

I GOT SOME SPIDERS, TOO-- 'COS THEY'RE QUICK AND SCARY, AND I HAD A *WASP*, BUT IT FLEW AWAY BEFORE I COULD GET ITS WINGS OFF.

THAT'S *HORRID*. WON'T THEY STARVE?

THEY MIGHT-- OR THEY MIGHT EAT EACH *OTHER*.

SOMETIMES I LET THEM OUT FOR EXER-CISE--BUT IF THEY TRY TO *ESCAPE* I EXECUTE THEM WITH THE DEAD-BOY'S HEART.

LIKE *THIS*

TCHUKK!

I'VE DONE LOTS. LOOK AT THE STAINS. IF I DO ENOUGH, THE DEAD-BOY'LL COME BACK AND SHOW ME THE WAY TO NEVER-NEVER LAND.

YOU'RE NASTY AND BAD, JOHN CONSTANTINE. LET THEM GO FREE--THEY'RE CREATURES, WITH FEELINGS. IT'S TERRIBLE CRUEL-EVIL.

'S NOT. IT'S JUSTICE.

LET THEM GO-- OR I'LL TELL ON YOU.

SO WHAT IF YOU DO. I'LL TELL UNCLE HARRY HOW I SEEN YOU LET YOUR KNICKERS DOWN TO RON SIMON FOR ONE-AND-SIXPENCE.

BUT I NEVER! IT'S NOT EVEN TRUE!

BUT HE'LL BELIEVE ME, THOUGH, WON'T HE? 'COS I'M A BOY!

WANT TO SEE ME KILL SOME MORE?

I HATE YOU.

DON'T CARE-- EVERYBODY DOES.

DIE...

DIE...DIE...

**TCHUKK!**

**TCHOKK!**

HEART-BEAT THROBS IN EXECUTED FINGER. EVERYTHING HURTS. EVERYTHING'S *SPOILED* NOW. EVERYTHING'S ALL DIRTY AND SMELLY AND SHITTY.

IT'S THE DEAD-BOY'S HEART. CHERYL'S RIGHT, IT IS CRUEL-EVIL. IT'S MAGIC -- BUT IT'S *BAD!*

SHOULDN'T'VE TOOK IT AWAY. WHAT IF HE *DOES* COME BACK LOOKING FOR IT? WHAT IF HE WANTS TO *SWAP?*

IT'S *WARM* NOW. HEAVIER WITH ALL THE PAIN IT'S SOAKED UP -- STICKY WITH INSECT-JUICE AND BLOOD.

STOP IT. IT'S *CURSED*. IT'S MAKING YOU DO BAD THINGS. GET RID OF IT. TAKE IT BACK.

102

TAKE IT BACK TO THE QUARRY-- WITH THE SCRUFFY BUSHES, THE FLIES, THE SHITS AND THE MOLDY DIRTY-BOOKS...

TAKE IT BACK TO THE DEAD-BOY. SEND IT DOWN TO HIM, THROUGH THE BOTTOMLESS LAKE TO NEVER-NEVER LAND.

GET RID OF IT BEFORE THE BOGEYMAN FINDS OUT IT'S GONE AND COMES TO GET IT BACK--AND TELLS YOU THE SECRET YOU DON'T WANT TO KNOW.

THROW IT HARD, HIGH-- OUT OVER THE WATER... HAND SWEATY. GRIP SLIPS, AS IF IT *TWITCHED*.

AND WATCH IT FALL DOWN... DOWN.

NO, *FURTHER*-- IT'S GOING TO HIT...

KRANNG!

WHY DOESN'T HE COME OUT--ROARING AND BELLOWING? HE *ALWAYS* COMES OUT.

TIN ROOF, THE SOUND-- OH JESUS, IT WENT STRAIGHT *THROUGH*.

IT HIT HIM--SPLIT HIS SKULL. HIS BRAINS' VE SPLASHED OUT--AND BLOOD--ALL DOWN HIS FACE, LIKE PORRIDGE AND JAM.

HE'S DEAD-- MUST BE. I'VE KILLED THE BOGEYMAN.

JOHN CONSTANTINE

# HELLBLAZER

HELLBLAZER 56
US $1.75
CAN $2.25 UK £1
AUGUST 1992

SUGGESTED FOR
MATURE READERS

GARTH ENNIS

DAVID LLOYD

DANNY DRAKE COULDN'T KEEP ANYTHING TO HIMSELF... SECRETS STEWED INSIDE HIM LIKE POISON AND WOUND HIM UP 'TIL HE WAS *MAD* WITH ANXIETY – CHRIST, HE ALWAYS HAD TO TELL *SOMEONE* –

SO HE WROTE IT ALL DOWN.

WHATEVER HE DID AND HOW HE FELT ABOUT IT, EVEN THAT AUGUST NIGHT WHEN THE FLOOR RAN SLICK WITH SOMETHING PINK AND WARM, AND WASN'T IT SO MUCH BETTER TO GET EVERYTHING OFF HIS CHEST?

THIS IS THE DIARY OF DANNY DRAKE

DANNY DOESN'T LIKE THE TUBE.

NORMALLY HE WOULDN'T GO NEAR IT, BUT LAST NIGHT HE LOST CONTROL OF THE BMW — HE JUST COULDN'T STOP SCREAMING - AND HE WRAPPED IT 'ROUND A LAMPPOST.

SO THE TUBE IT IS... HE WOULD SAY THINGS CAN'T GET ANY WORSE...

BUT HE KNOWS THEY CAN. AND WILL.

RIGHT NOW.

I'M A WHOREMONGER!

I-I AM! I USED TO DRIVE TO KING'S CROSS, OR DOWN TO THE EMBANK-MENT! I PICKED UP WOMEN! I PAID FOR IT!

IT WAS WHEN DAPHNE WAS PREGNANT - I WANTED IT SO BAD! I CAUGHT THE CLAP, AND, AND I HAD TO GO TO THE CLINIC!

WILL YOU SHUT UP, FOR CHRIST'S SAKE?

I CAN'T SHUT UP, YOU STUPID BASTARD!

I CAN'T!!

GET OUT! I'VE GOTTA GET OUT!

AND THE PAIN! AND IT DIDN'T STOP ME, I JUST WENT BACK FOR MORE! MORE SCREWING SLUTS IN ALLEYWAYS AND GOD DAMN ME, MORE!

OH, LET ME OUUTTT!

AND DAPHNE FOUND OUT, JUST LIKE SHE FOUND MY GRIMORIUM AND SHE CALLED ME A SHIT! A DIRTY LITTLE SHIT!

THANK CHRIST!

GRIMORIUM...

JUST...JUST LIKE...LAST TIME —

IS THIS... PUNISHMENT?

BLOODY SILLY ONE IF IT IS, MATE. YOU LOOKED A *RIGHT* ARSEHOLE.

PISS OFF! WHAT THE FRIG DO *YOU* KNOW ABOUT IT?

WELL...

I KNOW WHAT YOUR BOOK IS, THE ONE YOU SAID DAPHNE FOUND. ALL ABOUT A VERY NASTY PLACE, AND THE PEOPLE WHO LIVE THERE.

AND HOW TO SPEAK TO THEM.

START TALKING.

I'M JOHN CONSTANTINE. HE SAYS HE'S DANNY DRAKE. I'D HAVE BEEN HAPPY TO TALK IN A PUB, BUT HE WANTS TO GO HOME...

SODDING WALK TO MUSWELL HILL KNACKERS ME.

I'VE GOT TO GET BACK TO MY HOUSE... IF I - WHEN I FREAK OUT AGAIN I DON'T WANT PEOPLE TO SEE...

I REALLY HOPE I CAN TRUST YOU~

OH, FOR SURE. ASK ANYONE.

ART LOVER. FINE TASTES.

BET HE SMOKES ENOUGH DOPE TO RAISE THE DEAD...

I'LL MAKE SOME COFFEE.

HE DROPS THE CUPS ONCE AND THE SUGARBOWL TWICE WHILE HE'S MAKING IT. NOT A GOOD SIGN.

IT JUST SEEMS SO...SO INSANE...

BUT I SUPPOSE YOU'RE USED TO HEARING STRANGE STUFF.

I'M BEING HAUNTED BY MY DIARY.

YOUR DIARY...? WHY? YOU BEEN SEEING SOMEONE BEHIND ITS BACK?

PLEASE DON'T JOKE.

I MUST HAVE BEEN KEEPING A DIARY FOR OVER TEN YEARS NOW. IT WAS ALWAYS SUCH A RELIEF TO HAVE SOMEWHERE TO PUT ALL MY SECRETS, YOU KNOW? TO STOP THEM...NAGGING AT ME...

"I ALWAYS WROTE LOADS. EVERYTHING WENT DOWN, EVEN THE STUFF I'D NEVER DARE TELL ANOTHER PERSON...

"THAT WAS WHAT THE DIARY WAS FOR.

"IT BECAME LIKE A FRIEND, A MATE I COULD TRUST WITH ANYTHING. I DID PRETTY WELL IN THE EIGHTIES — PLAYING THE MARKETS AND SO ON — AND THERE WAS DAPHNE, TOO. WELL, BEFORE SHE LEFT."

"THEY WERE GOOD TIMES. WE'D SIT AND GO OVER THEM TOGETHER, AND HAVE A LAUGH..."

ME AND THE DIARY, I MEAN.

WHAT ABOUT DAPHNE?

AH, WELL. MY WIFE. WALKED OUT ON ME A FEW YEARS BACK...I'VE MET SOMEONE ELSE SINCE, THOUGH.

THAT'S WHERE THE TROUBLE STARTED.

"OPHELIA WAS ONE IN A MILLION.

"FIRST OF ALL, SHE WAS GORGEOUS. A REAL LOOKER, YOU KNOW? I DIDN'T THINK SHE'D WANT MUCH TO DO WITH ME...

"BUT SHE DID."

YOU KNOW, I USED TO PREFER WHAT WE DID AFTERWARDS TO THE SEX ITSELF...

OH?

WE TALKED.

"THAT WAS THE OTHER THING ABOUT 'PHEE – SHE WAS SUCH A GOOD LISTENER. I COULD TELL HER ANYTHING, EVEN SOME OF THE OLD STUFF FROM MY DIARY, AND SHE WOULDN'T MIND."

"SHE WAS THE ONE I WENT TO WHEN I FELT DEPRESSED, OR GUILTY, OR ROTTEN. SHE SHELTERED ME."

"AND AFTER A WHILE...WELL, WHO NEEDED A DIARY WITH 'PHEE AROUND?"

YEAH, I THINK I'VE TWIGGED WHAT'S COMING NEXT...

I KNOW IT WAS STUPID, BUT I THOUGHT IT WOULD DO ME GOOD...I DIDN'T HAVE TO RECORD MY LIFE LIKE I WAS A SCHOOLBOY OR SOMETHING.

I COULD TALK TO A REAL PERSON.

THEN SHE LEFT ME.

"SHE SAID SHE LIKED. ME, BUT I WAS TOO FEEBLE. SAID WHAT I NEEDED WAS SOMEONE TO KICK ME INTO GEAR RATHER THAN A SHOULDER TO CRY ON."

"JESUS, WHAT DID SHE MEAN?"

I WAS SO MISERABLE, I FORGOT THE DIARY COMPLETELY...

THE FIRST TIME IT HAPPENED, I WAS ON THE PHONE.

I DON'T KNOW, ROBIN. I MIGHT POP IN...YEAH, MAYBE IT *WOULD* CHEER ME UP TO GO TO A PARTY, BUT—

UH.

ROBIN... ...DID I EVER TELL YOU I PISS IN THE SINK?

I DO! SOMETIMES IF I'M REALLY DRUNK I JUST, I JUST CAN'T HELP IT — I HARDLY KNOW WHERE I AM AND I *PISS IN THE SINK!*

IN THE SINK, FOR CHRIST'S SAKE! *THE SINK!*

I HADN'T BEEN ABLE TO STOP MYSELF. I *HAD* TO SAY IT.

LIKE ON THE TUBE?

MM. BUT IT WAS JUST THE START...

I *HATE* YOUR BREAD PUDDING, MOTHER! I'VE ALWAYS FRIGGING HATED IT!

I'M GOING HOME!

I BUY WANKMAGS! *KIDDIE PORN! BESTIALITY!*

I'M A *PERVERT!*

I SCORED LAST WEEK, LADS! TWO OUNCES! JAMAICAN! BLEW ME AWAY!

IT WAS THE STUFF I NEVER TOLD ANYONE, NOT EVEN DAPHNE OR 'PHEE. ONLY ONE WHO KNEW ABOUT IT WAS ME...

...AND THE DIARY.

ALL RIGHT, HANG ON. SO FAR YOU'VE TOLD ME ABOUT YOUR DIARY AND A FEW DAFT THINGS YOU GET UP TO. ...WHERE DOES THE MAGIC COME INTO IT?

BUT DON'T YOU SEE? THE DIARY'S THE ONLY OTHER ONE THAT KNOWS! IT'S MAKING ME DO IT!

UNLESS YOU'RE GOING 'ROUND THE BEND...

LET'S HEAR ABOUT THE MAGIC.

YOU...YOU DO BELIEVE IN THIS STUFF? REALLY?

DO I EVER. GET ON WITH IT.

I...ALL THE MONEY FOR MY HOUSE, I MEAN, MY JOB, ALL MY THINGS...THEY —WELL, THEY DIDN'T EXACTLY COME FROM HARD WORK.

"IT STARTED AT UNIVERSITY. ME AND A FEW MATES GOT INTO SOME MINOR STUFF – NOTHING ACTUALLY WORKED, BUT IT WAS A LAUGH. SOMETHING TO DO.

"I WAS THE ONLY ONE WHO STUCK WITH IT. I GOT THE FEELING THERE WAS SOMETHING BETTER HERE THAN WHAT EVERYDAY LIFE COULD OFFER...

"IT TOOK ME A MONTH TO UNDERSTAND A SINGLE PAGE OF THE GRIMORIUM.

"IT WAS THE LAST DAY OF AUGUST, ABOUT TEN YEARS AGO, REALLY HOT... I REMEMBER THINKING WE WERE IN FOR AN INDIAN SUMMER.

"ITS NAME WAS TRISKELE. IT GAVE ME LUCK – A GOLDEN TOUCH IN TRADE AND FINANCE – AND ALL IT COST ME WAS ETERNAL LIFE.

"I TOLD MY DIARY THAT, AS WELL."

WHAT DO I SAY TO THIS IDIOT?

THIS SAD, STUPID BASTARD WHO'S FALLEN FOR THE OLDEST TRICK—

YOU NEVER MISS YOUR SOUL 'TIL YOU'VE SIGNED IT AWAY.

OKAY, DANNY...

I'M GOING TO DO A BIT OF SNIFFING ABOUT, YOU STAY HERE – DON'T GO OUT, JUST IN CASE YOU START CONFESSING YOUR SINS AGAIN.

WHAT...?

WAIT! DON'T LEAVE ME ALONE!

FOR CHRIST'S SAKE, DANNY! LEAVE OFF!

I'M GOING TO TRY TO FIND OUT ABOUT YOUR DEMON, AND THEN I'LL SEE IF IT'S THE ONE MAKING YOU SPOUT OUT BITS OF YOUR DIARY, OKAY?

SOMETIMES THEY MESS YOU ABOUT WHEN YOU'RE UNDER CONTRACT. THEY THINK IT'S FUNNY.

NOW SIT DOWN, WAIT FOR ME, AND RELAX.

JESUS!

MY COPY OF THE GRIMORIUM'S IN CHAS'S LOCK-UP. KIT DOESN'T LIKE ME KEEPING IT AT HER FLAT, AND CHAS TOLD EVERYONE DOWN THE RED ROVER I WAS UNDER THE THUMB...

I SAID I'D TURN 'EM ALL INTO FROGS.

DROP THE KEYS BACK TO US, OKAY?

NO ONE DARED LAUGH.

CHEERS, CHAS.

NEEDS A LITTLE CELLOTAPE...

BOLLOCKS...!

BUT THIS COPY HAS A BONUS: BEN COX'S NOTES.

BEN READ EVERYTHING FROM THE SATANIC BIBLE TO THE KEY OF SOLOMON, AND EVERYTHING HE FOUND OUT ABOUT DEMONS HE NOTED IN HERE...

THANKS, BEN. SORRY.

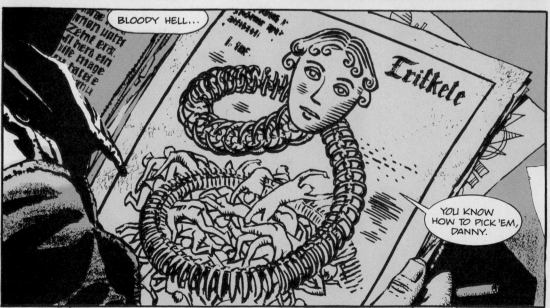

BLOODY HELL...

Tritkele

YOU KNOW HOW TO PICK 'EM, DANNY.

LET'S SEE...TRISKELE, WYRM QUEEN OF SUCCUBAÉ, THE BITCH SPIRIT WHO KILLED A HUNDRED SERAPHIM...JESUS.

WHAT'S THIS...? SLAYER OF THE ARCHANGEL DARIEL, WHOSE FACE SHE TORE OFF AND WORE AS HER OWN...

SCREW ME, DANNY! WHY DIDN'T YOU JUST GO STRAIGHT TO THE FIRST OF THE FALLEN AND HAVE DONE WITH IT?!

DANNY'S SUCH A WEIRD LITTLE BASTARD ANYWAY ...I WANT TO HELP HIM 'COS I KNOW HOW IT FEELS TO BE THIS DEEP IN SHIT - AND I HATE BLOODY DEMONS –

BUT THE GUY IS SO SLIMY AND PATHETIC, AND I GET THE FEELING THERE'S MORE TO ALL THIS.

SOD IT. READ ON. SEE WHAT OTHER SURPRISES LIE IN STORE...

SHIT!

122

WHA...?

TRISKELE, DANNY. SHE'S A GREEDY BITCH. SHE'S FAMOUS FOR IT.

IN FACT, SHE *NEVER* ALLOWS A MORTAL TO KEEP HIS SOUL FOR MORE THAN *FIVE* YEARS. ONCE YOU SIGN THE CONTRACT, THE CLOCK STARTS TICKING.

A HOT AUGUST NIGHT TEN YEARS AGO, YOU SAID...

HOW DID YOU GET YOUR *EXTRA* FIVE?

I, I'M NOT SAYING — I DON'T EVEN KNOW WHAT YOU MEAN—

JUST GET THE HELL OUT OF MY HOUSE, ALL RIGHT?!

ALL RIGHT, DANNY. ALL RIGHT.

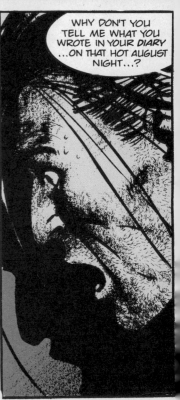

WHY DON'T YOU TELL ME WHAT YOU WROTE IN YOUR *DIARY* ...ON THAT HOT AUGUST NIGHT...?

"THE NIGHT ARRIVED, AND THERE WAS NO ESCAPING IT. GOD, I WAS SICK 'TIL MY THROAT BLED...

"TRISKELE WAS COMING FOR ME.

"ME ...OR SOMETHING BETTER.

"SOMETHING I COULD GIVE HER - SOMETHING SHE'D WANT - THAT SHE'D ACCEPT INSTEAD.

"DAPHNE WAS JUST ANOTHER FRIGGING SINNER, NO GOOD AT ALL - BUT THEN I REMEMBERED —

"OUR UNBORN CHLD.

"OUR INNOCENT UNBORN CHILD.

"I CUT HER THROAT AND RIPPED THAT CHILD OUT OF HER, AND TRISKELE LICKED HIM UP LIKE HE WAS SUGAR."

FIVE MORE YEARS.

CELLAR'S THROUGH HERE, IS IT?

WHAT? WAIT!

DON'T GO IN THERE!

THIS IS WHERE YOU DID IT, DANNY. BIT OF PRIVACY, EASY TO CARRY DAPHNE DOWN HERE.

TRISKELE'S GETTING AT YOU, LIKE I THOUGHT. USING THE DIARY...

WHY?

eeeeeee

NOT THAT! NOT THAT!

eeeeeeee!

SSSHH, BE OKAY. BE FINE.

SSSHH, NOW.

TRISKELE'S TELLING YOU YOUR TIME'S UP AGAIN, ISN'T SHE? IS IT TONIGHT?

YES. OH JESUS, YES—

WHERE'D YOU NICK THE KID?

COVENT GARDEN, SOME WOMAN LEFT THE PRAM OUTSIDE A CHEESE SHOP, BUT LOOK—

YOU'D BETTER STAY HERE, DANNY...

...'COS IF YOU TRY TO GET OUT OF THIS HOUSE TONIGHT, I'LL KILL YOU.

I LEFT THE BABY WITH THE OLD BILL. "FOUND HER IN AN ALLEY DOWN NEAR COVENT GARDEN, CONSTABLE. YOUNG WOMEN THESE DAYS SHOULD FACE UP TO THEIR RESPONSIBILITIES, BLAH-FRIGGING-BLAH."

HULLO, JOHN.

WHY DID I EVEN TRY TO HELP THAT ARSEHOLE?

GIN AND TONIC, INNIT?

NOT TONIGHT, TOM. WHISKY.

WELL, SCREW HIM. THE LITTLE SHIT SOLD HIS SOUL. HE MURDERED HIS WIFE.

HE SENT AN INNOCENT TO HELL — FOR CHRIST'S SAKE, HE WAS GOING TO DO IT AGAIN, TONIGHT—

BUT A LONG TIME AGO... IN A PLACE CALLED NEWCASTLE...

ROUGH NIGHT, JOHN?

...SO DID I.

YEAH, CHAS.

ROUGH NIGHT.

THE END

I'M DROPPING YOU OFF AT THE HOUSE WHILE I FETCH THEM.

SHIT, CHAS--I SAID I WANTED TO GO TO TOTTENHAM.

TOUGH. NO TIME. I'LL TAKE YOU LATER.

C'MON, MATE--YOU *KNOW* I'M BOX-OFFICE POISON WHERE RENEE'S CONCERNED. AND I'M CRAP WITH *BABIES* AND STUFF...

STOP WHINING. ANYWAY, I'D SORT OF LIKE IT IF YOU SAW THE KID, JOHN. RENEE'S GOT HUNDREDS OF RELATIVES AND I'VE ONLY...

WELL, I HAVEN'T--YOU KNOW?

ALL RIGHT, DON'T START CRYING. I'M GETTING A LUMP IN ME THROAT, AND I DON'T WANT TO THROW UP IN YOUR CAB.

I S'POSE IT WON'T HURT TO WET THE BABY'S HEAD--LONG AS YOU'VE GOT SOME DECENT GIN.

THANKS, JOHN. YOU'RE A MATE.

I DON'T WANT TO COUNT THE YEARS SINCE I LAST CLIMBED THE STEPS TO "QUEENIE'S CASTLE," BUT IT MUST BE MORE THAN TWENTY. I WAS FRESH DOWN FROM LIVERPOOL AND STUCK FOR A PLACE TO CRASH.

CHAS AND HIS MISSUS HAVE TRIED TO TART THE OLD HELL-HOUSE UP. USED TO BE ALL SNOT-GREEN PAINTWORK-- AND A SCABBY YARD FULL OF SODDEN MATTRESSES AND OLD WRINGERS TANGLED WITH SOOTY ELDER TREES.

PLACE STILL GIVES ME THE SHITS, THOUGH. SOME THINGS YOU CAN'T DISGUISE WITH COSMETICS. LIKE DEATH. EVER SEEN A CORPSE AFTER THE EMBALMER'S THROUGH WITH IT?

GIVE ME GOOD, HONEST PUTREFACTION, ANYTIME.

FOR A SECOND, THAT FAMILIAR, SWEET DREAD RIPPLES MY HEART WITH EXCITEMENT, AS I PART THE SICKLY, VIOLET LIPS OF THE DOOR AND THE HOUSE EXHALES IN MY FACE.

BUT THE STINK THAT SLIPS ITS FINGERS DOWN MY THROAT IS NOT THE HALITOSIS OF CORRUPTION--IT'S THICK, CHEMICAL LAVENDER...

BLOODY AIR FRESHENER.

SHE KEEPS A NEAT HOUSE, DOES RENEE. YOU'D HAVE TO BE CAREFUL WHERE YOU FLICKED YOUR ASH 'ROUND HERE...

WHICH REMINDS ME...

WHILE THE KETTLE BOILS FOR COFFEE, I SCOUT AROUND FOR SMOKES. IF I KNOW CHAS, HE'LL HAVE SOME STASHED IN CASE OF EMERGENCY.

BINGO...WITH HIS DIRTY VIDEOS--SAFE OUT OF RENEE'S SIGHT.

POOR OLD CHAS. SHE KEEPS HIM ON A PRETTY SHORT ROPE. PERSONALLY, I'D SOONER TOP MYSELF THAN LIVE LIKE THIS--BUT HE SEEMS TO THRIVE ON IT, BLESS 'IM.

RENEE'S A STRANGE ONE. I SCREWED HER A COUPLE OF TIMES-- BEFORE SHE MARRIED CHAS--BUT SHE NEVER LIKED ME.

I RECKON IT WAS HIM SHE WAS AFTER ALL ALONG--ONLY SHE WAS SCARED OF ME, AND HAD TO PUT ME IN MY PLACE.

WOMEN CAN BE WEIRD. THEY MOVE IN MYSTERIOUS WAYS. A SMART BLOKE CAN LEARN A LOT FROM THEM--IF HE KEEPS HIS NERVE.

AND RENEE WAS RIGHT. I *WAS* A "BAD INFLUENCE," AND CHAS *WAS* ALWAYS IN LOVE WITH ME-- ALTHOUGH HE'D KICK YOUR FACE IN IF YOU TOLD HIM SO.

IT'S NOT UNTIL I REACH THE FIRST LANDING THAT IT OCCURS TO ME TO WONDER WHY I'M GOING UPSTAIRS. I'M IN A WEIRD MOOD--DETACHED, EDGY, SLIGHTLY VULNERABLE.

FUCKING JET LAG, I EXPECT.

THIS WAS MY ROOM FOR A YEAR. MUST BE CHAS AND RENEE'S NOW. I'M ABOUT TO GO IN WHEN A PERI-PHERAL FLICKER...A TRANSIENT PUNGENCY...A SENSE OF *SCAMPERING*...

--SHIT, SOMETHING INDEFINABLE--ATTRACTS ME TO THE SECOND FLIGHT OF STAIRS. THE ONE THAT LEADS TO THE ROOM AT THE TOP OF THE HOUSE.

THE ROOM THAT *QUEENIE* USED TO LIVE IN, WITH HER DISGUSTING MONKEY, "SLAG."

QUEENIE WAS CHAS' MUM. SHE WAS A MONSTROUS, VILE, MANIPULATIVE OLD WITCH--AND THAT'S THE HARSH BUT SIMPLE TRUTH. SHE SCARED THE LIVING SHIT OUT OF ME.

QUEENIE WAS *DREADFUL*--IN THE OLDEST SENSE OF THE WORD.

AND AS FOR HER BLEEDIN' *FAMILIAR*...

A CHITINOUS SCRATCHING ON THE SKYLIGHT ERECTS MY BODY HAIR. MUSCLES TENSE INVOLUNTARILY.

PROBABLY JUST STARLINGS...

THIS MUST BE GERALDINE'S ROOM NOW--ALL DONE UP FOR THE NEW KID. SHIT, SHE'S GOT HER BED RIGHT WHERE QUEENIE'S USED TO FESTER.

NO SENSE, NO FEELING, *eh, CHAS?*

FANCY LETTING YOUR DAUGHTER AND GRANDCHILD LIVE IN A ROOM SPLATTERED WITH *THIS ONE'S* PSYCHIC CRUD--

AND GOD KNOWS WHAT *OTHER* VILE EFFLUVIUM, AS WELL.

THE FIRST TIME I EVER STEPPED INTO QUEENIE'S ROOM, I GOT HIT SMACK IN THE FACE BY A HANDFUL OF SHIT. I THINK IT WAS THE MONKEY WHO THREW IT, BUT I'VE NEVER BEEN COMPLETELY SURE.

THEY WERE BOTH LAUGHING, ANYWAY-- CACKLING LIKE A BRACE OF DEMONS ON AMPHETAMINE. NEARLY STOPPED ME BLOODY HEART. 'COURSE, I'VE SEEN WORSE SINCE, BUT I WAS STILL WET BEHIND THE EARS BACK THEN.

YOU MUST BE THE NEW LODGER--JOHNNIE, AIN'T IT?

JOHN.

WELL, WIPE YOUR MUSH ON THEM CURTAINS, JOHNNIE, AN' COME OVER 'ERE SO ME AN' SLAG CAN 'AVE A BUTCHER'S AT YOU.

WHAT D'YOU RECKON, GIRL-- PRETTY-BOY, AIN'T HE?

HE'S A SISSY. BET HE AIN'T GOT A GOOD SHAG IN 'IM.

HUH! IT TALKED...

YOU WHAT?

THAT FUCKING MONKEY TALKED.

DON'T BE A SOFT TWAT. SLAG'S A *MONKEY*. IF SHE COULD *TALK*, WE'D BE RICH AND NOT 'AVE TO RENT ROOMS TO DAFT TURDS LIKE YOU.

'COS SHE *IS* ONE, DOPEY.

YEAH...ANYWAY, NICE CHATTING WITH YOU, QUEENIE...

RIGHT. SO, UH-- HOW COME YOU CALL THE MONKEY *SLAG*?

HOLD YOUR BLEEDIN' 'ORSES. WHERE'S THAT LITTLE WANKER OF A BOY OF MINE?

WHO, CHAS...? HE WENT OUT. DOWN THE PUB, I THINK.

OH *DID* HE?

SLAG--GO AN' FETCH THE SNEAKY FUCKER BACK.

MEANTIME, *YOU'LL* 'AVE TO DO THE HONORS, JOHNNIE BOY. ME PISSPOT'S FULL AN' ME BACK TEETH'RE AFLOAT...

BUT *FIRST*, REACH UNDER ME SHEETS AN' HELP ME FIND ME CIGGIES. I'VE LOST 'EM, AN' I CAN'T MOVE ME LEGS NO MORE.

*NO BLOODY CHANCE, MISSUS.*

YOU'D BETTER, OR I'LL SQUASH YOUR LITTLE BALLS LIKE SPARRER'S EGGS--SAME AS I WILL ANY TIME YOU TRY TO CROSS ME OR POKE YOUR BEAK INTO THINGS THAT DON'T CONCERN YOU.

OLD SLAG MIGHTN'T THINK THAT MUCH OF YOU, JACK-THE-BLEEDIN'-LAD --BUT YOU'VE GOT BADNESS IN YOUR EYES.

JUST YOU REMEMBER, OLD QUEENIE'S DEALT WITH CLEVER-DICKS LIKE YOU BEFORE.

I'M SORRY, JOHN.

JESUS CHRIST, CHAS-- YOU COULD'VE WARNED ME.

YOU WOULDN'T 'AVE MOVED IN, IF I 'AD.

AN' I DID TELL YOU ME MUM LIVED HERE AS WELL...

YOU NEVER MENTIONED THE SODDIN' MONKEY, DID YOU? DOES IT REALLY COME AND FETCH YOU OUT OF THE PUB?

IT DOESN'T ACTUALLY COME IN--JUST MAKES THE FUCKIN' AWFUL STINK OF TOILETS HANG AROUND ME 'TILL IT GETS SO EMBARRASSING I HAVE TO LEAVE. AIN'T YOU EVER NOTICED IT?

"IT'S ALWAYS WAITING OUTSIDE--UP A LAMP-POST, OR SOMEWHERE-- FIDDLING WITH ITS FANNY."

RED LION

IT'S NOT FUCKIN' *FUNNY,* JOHN.

NO, MATE, I'LL BET IT'S NOT.

I CAN'T DO *NOTHIN'* WITHOUT QUEENIE FINDING OUT ABOUT IT. SLAG'S HER BLEEDIN' EYES AN' EARS-- ALWAYS *SPYING* ON ME, BUGGERING THINGS UP.

LIKE, YOU KNOW THAT LITTLE GREEK GIRL FROM THE CHIP SHOP?

WELL, I TOOK HER TO THE PICTURES LAST WEEK, AND GUESS WHAT? SHE *LIKED* ME.

SO WE COME BACK HERE, AND BEFORE YOU KNOW IT, WE'RE ON THE SOFA, *DOING* IT--Y'KNOW?

I'VE SEEN *PICTURES...*

NOT *THIS* SORT OF SHIT, YOU AIN'T.

I'M ABOUT TEN SECONDS FROM THE VINEGAR STROKE WHEN I FEEL IT LAND ON MY BACK.

FEEL WHAT, MATE?

BLOODY *SLAG,* OF COURSE.

"THE BLEEDIN' MONKEY WAS RIDING ME LIKE A COWBOY --SMOKIN' A CIGGIE, SLAPPIN' ME ARSE, AND WHOOPING AND HOLLERING, WITH A FINGER STUCK UP ME TACK HOLE..."

'COURSE, THE GREEK BIRD 'AD TO PAINT ME THE FULL PICTURE, AFTER SHE'D CALMED DOWN.

I KNEW ABOUT THE FINGER, MIND YOU-- BUT I THOUGHT IT WAS HERS.

I'M WARNING YOU, CONSTANTINE... I WOULDN'T TELL THIS TO ANOTHER LIVIN' SOUL. IF YOU LAUGH AT ME, I'LL BATTER YOU.

'COURSE, I DID LAUGH, HYSTERICALLY-- BUT HE DIDN'T BATTER ME. HE JUST OPENED UP THE SAD, WRAPPED TURD OF HIS LIFE FOR ME, AND LAID IT ON MY PLATE.

QUEENIE WAS NEVER THE SAME AS THE OTHER KIDS' MUMS. IN THEIR HOUSES, IT WAS THE DADS GOT DRUNK AN' DID THE THUMPING.

"MY OLD MAN WAS THIS QUIET LITTLE BLOKE -- OR MAYBE HE JUST SEEMED THAT WAY NEXT TO HER, 'CAUSE SHE WAS BIG AN' NOISY, AN' STRONG AS A BLEEDIN' 'ORSE.

144

"I DON'T REMEMBER 'IM THAT WELL--SHE KILLED 'IM WHEN I WAS SEVEN--CHUCKED A STOUT BOTTLE AT 'IM AN' KNOCKED 'IM DOWN THE BLOODY STAIRS."

"HE LAID IN 'IS BED COUGHING FOR A WEEK BEFORE HE DIED. SAYS *PNEUMONIA* ON THE DEATH CERTIFICATE. THAT WAS 1960-- SAME YEAR ME BIG BROTHER, TERRY, GOT 'ANGED..."

SO IT WAS JUST ME AN' QUEENIE, THEN.

WHERE WAS THE *MONKEY?*

SHE GOT THAT A BIT LATER. I ASKED HER WHERE IT COME FROM, ONCE.

SAME PLACE AS YOU DID, YOU LITTLE TURD. FOUND 'ER IN THE TOILET PAN, AFTER I'D DONE ME BUSINESS.

"ONCE SHE HAD THE BLASTED APE TO SNOOP FOR HER, SHE DIDN'T EVEN BOTHER GETTING OUT OF BED."

"SHE'D ALREADY STOPPED DOING THE *ABORTIONS*--BUT SHE STILL HAD A GOOD BUSINESS WITH THE *CHARMS*. Y'KNOW, LOVE SPELLS, BABY-MAKING POTIONS, LIMP-PRICK PILLS TO KEEP THE OLD MAN QUIET..."

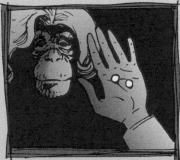

"AND THE *SEANCES*--FOR THIRTY BOB A TIME, SHE'D LET THEM GOSSIP WITH DEAD RELATIVES. SHE SPECIALIZED IN *WIDOWS* WHOSE BLOKES WERE KILLED IN THE *WAR*."

I THOUGHT THEY BURNED ALL THE WITCHES IN THE MIDDLE AGES.

I WISH TO GOD THEY FUCKIN' *HAD*, JOHN. SHE'S MADE MY LIFE SHEER BLOODY *HELL*--

SQUATTIN' UP THERE FOR TEN YEARS, LIKE SOME BIG, COLD *TOAD*--MAKING ME FETCH AN' CARRY FOR HER, AN' KEEP HER *CLEAN*...

YOU COULD'VE DONE A BETTER JOB *THERE*, MATE.

AN' SHE JUST KEEPS GETTING FOULER, AND *MADDER*...

NOBODY COMES ANYMORE. THEY'RE TOO SCARED NOW. THEY USE HER TO FRIGHTEN THEIR KIDS -- "BEHAVE, OR I'LL SEND YOU UP TO *QUEENIE'S CASTLE!*"

CHRIST, I HATE HER, JOHN. WHAT AM I GOING TO *DO?* SHE'S MADE ME A FUCKIN' *SLAVE.*

YOU COULD PUT HER IN A *HOME*, OR SOMETHING--SO SHE COULD GET SOME PROPER LOOKING AFTER. THAT ROOM COULD START A *CHOLERA* EPIDEMIC.

SHE'D *KILL* ME IF I TRIED--OR WORSE. JUST THINKING ABOUT IT GIVES ME THE SHITS.

YOU DON'T KNOW WHAT SHE CAN *DO*, JOHN.

SHE CAN JUST *LOOK* AT YOU AND, LIKE, FILL YOU UP WITH *FEAR*--AN' IF SHE DOES THE TRANCE THING, THIS WHITE STRINGY STUFF STARTS WRIGGLING OUT OF ALL HER HOLES, AN' KIND OF TANGLES YOU UP...

'STREWTH! WHAT, LIKE *ECTOPLASM*?

SHE CALLS IT "SPIRIT SPUNK." IT'S 'ORRIBLE, MATE.

WHY DON'T YOU JUST PISS OFF SOMEWHERE, FOR GOOD?

I TRIED IT. SHE SENT THE MONKEY. IT MADE THE SMELL SO BAD, PEOPLE WERE PUKING IN THE STREET.

HMMMM... I S'POSE KILLING HER'S OUT OF THE *QUESTION*...?

PRIMAL TERROR. SEXUAL DREAD. RITES OF PASSAGE...BACK THEN, I NEVER THOUGHT MUCH ABOUT BOLLOCKS LIKE THAT.

AN OLDER, WISER MAN MIGHT HAVE FOUND A MORE SUBTLE ANGLE--BUT I WAS A HOT-BLOODED POST-ADOLESCENT MALE. MY FRIEND WAS IN TROUBLE, SO I JUST WADED IN.

'COURSE, I WASN'T BEING TOTALLY ALTRUISTIC. I'D BEEN INTO SPOOKY SHIT SINCE I WAS A KID, BUT I'D NEVER HAD A REAL MAGICAL ENEMY TO TRY MYSELF AGAINST, BEFORE.

TO BE HONEST, I WAS BEGGING FOR IT. ALONG WITH THE FREE LOVE AND ROCK'N'ROLL, THIS WAS WHAT I'D LEFT HOME LOOKING FOR.

AND ON THE BOTTOM LINE, I SUPPOSE I MUST'VE KNOWN INSTINCTIVELY THAT, IF I FREED CHAS FROM QUEENIE'S SPELL --GOT THE MONKEY OFF HIS BACK--I'D HAVE A FRIEND FOR LIFE.

AND FRIENDS ARE ALWAYS USEFUL.

TOOK ME A MONTH TO FIGURE IT OUT AND WORK UP THE NERVE TO DO IT. I NEVER SAID A WORD TO CHAS. HE DIDN'T UNDERSTAND MAGIC. IT FREAKED HIM OUT.

HE JUST WANTED A STRAIGHT, SIMPLE LIFE --AND ANYWAY, YOU COULDN'T REALLY EXPECT A BLOKE TO HELP YOU DO IN HIS OLD MUM, EVEN IF IT WAS FOR HIS OWN GOOD.

AND EVERYBODY ELSE'S, TOO. THINK HOW HE MIGHT'VE TURNED OUT IF I HADN'T DONE IT. THEY'D PROBABLY BE CATCHING HIM ABOUT NOW-- WITH THIRTY BODIES BURIED IN THE YARD.

AND IT WASN'T THAT EASY FOR ME, EITHER. BASIC MAGICAL PRINCIPLE: THERE'S ALWAYS A PRICE.

I HAD TO GET OFF WITH THE BLEEDIN' MONKEY.

QUEENIE HAD MY CARD MARKED FROM THE START. I THINK SHE SAW ME AS SOME KIND OF A MINOR UPSTART--SHE KNEW I WAS TROUBLE, BUT THOUGHT SHE COULD EASILY SLAP MY ARSE.

I WAS JACK-THE-LAD, THOUGH. I PLAYED IT COOL, IGNORED THE INSULTS, MADE JOKES WITH HER--AND NEVER LET ON I WAS SHIT-SCARED, THE WAY CHAS DID.

AND THAT REALLY GOT ON HER TITS--MADE HER DESPERATE TO FIND A WEAKNESS. SO SHE LET SLAG LOOSE ON ME.

THE MONKEY WAS QUEENIE'S FAMILIAR --HER AGENT. IT WAS PART OF HER. SYMBIOTIC WAS A WORD I'D JUST LEARNED--IT SEEMED TO FIT.

IT SEEMS INSANELY ARROGANT NOW--BUT MAGIC'S SUCH A SQUIRMY, SEDUCTIVE THING, AND IT ALWAYS HAS ITS OWN KIND OF MAD, SUBJECTIVE LOGIC--

AND THE WAY I SAW IT, WITHOUT THE MONKEY FOR SUPPORT, THE OLD COW WOULDN'T HAVE A LEG TO STAND ON, SO TO SPEAK.

I HATED THAT APE WORSE THAN POISON. IT HAD A TONGUE THAT WAS PURE BLOODY EVIL. IT WAS ALWAYS HANGING AROUND ME, WHISPERING SHIT FROM JUST OUT OF RANGE.

TWISTED SEX STUFF, MOSTLY--STUFF TO MAKE YOU GENERALLY SICK, OR FURIOUS, OR SUDDENLY WANT TO CRY. BUT I DIDN'T DO NONE OF THAT. I LISTENED, SMILED POLITELY, AND STAYED CALM.

AFTER A COUPLE OF WEEKS I STARTED TO PAY IT THE ODD COMPLIMENT, TO FLIRT WITH IT--BUT IT'D NEVER COME WITHIN REACH. OLD SLAG DIDN'T TRUST ME. SHE WAS A WISE MONKEY.

I PUSHED IT A BIT, WENT ALL WAN AND MOODY--FEIGNED INFATUATION. CHRIST, I SHOULD'VE GOT A BLOODY OSCAR. CHAS THOUGHT I'D GONE BLOODY NUTS.

I GROVELLED FOR ATTENTION. I BROUGHT HER GIFTS: CIGARETTES ... STOCKINGS ...

SHE WORE THEM FOR ME, TOO, GOD HELP ME -- BUT STILL WOULDN'T LET ME TOUCH HER.

SO I MADE MYSELF SOB IN THE NIGHT, WHILE SHE SAT OUTSIDE, GIGGLING-- GETTING OFF ON MY "MISERY."

BUT THEN, ONE NIGHT, I DIDN'T GO BACK TO THE HOUSE. I WALKED TO THE CANAL, AND WAITED.

IT TOOK HER TWO HOURS TO FIND ME --BUT I KNEW I HAD HER THEN.

YOU'RE SO BEAUTIFUL. I'M IN LOVE WITH YOU. I CAN'T LIVE IF YOU DESPISE ME. I'LL HAVE TO DROWN MYSELF.

SHE WAS PUTTY IN MY HANDS.

I TELL YOU, MY HEART WAS IN MY MOUTH. SHE MIGHT'VE CALLED MY BLUFF.

BUT CLICHÉS ARE SOMETIMES DEADLY. SHE BOUGHT IT--SORT OF SMILED, AND LET DOWN HER GUARD.

AND I SQUEEZED THE RANK POWER FROM HER, INHALING IT IN THE BURSTING BUBBLES OF HER DROWNING BREATH, FEELING SNAKE-ROPES OF ECTOPLASM WRITHING AROUND ME --

KNOWING IT WAS BLACK MURDER I WAS DOING-- THAT QUEENIE WOULD BE DEAD BEFORE I GOT BACK HOME--

BUT HOLDING ON, EVEN THOUGH THE BLOOD HOWLED IN MY EARS-- AND A MOCKING VOICE CALLED FROM FAR AWAY...

OO-ER... LOOK, MUM, THERE'S A STRANGE MAN IN ME BED.

QUEENIE...?

WHO...?

NO, IT'S ME-- GERALDINE. DON'T YOU REMEMBER ME, UNCLE JOHN?

LOOK AT THAT! I *KNEW* IT--THE BASTARD'S ONLY GONE AN' BURNED A RUDDY GREAT HOLE IN THE NEW *CARPET.*

SHIT. SORRY, RENEE.

LOOKS LIKE YOU BLEW IT, JOHN. WHAT YOU KIPPIN' UP *HERE* FOR, ANYWAY?

NARCOLEPTIC EPISODE --ALWAYS HANDY FOR DUCKING OUT OF SITUATIONS OF MORAL STRESS, Y'KNOW?

NOT REALLY, MATE.

OH WELL, C'EST LA GUERRE...

THIS THE NEW *SPROG,* THEN?

YEAH--AIN'T SHE BLOODY *GORGEOUS?*

PRETTY AS A PICTURE--JUST LIKE HER GRANDMA.

'E'S *NOT* STAYING.

DO YOU *REALLY* THINK SHE'S PRETTY?

IT'S WEIRD, AFTER I'D 'AD HER AND THE NURSE GAVE HER TO ME TO HOLD--I LOOKED DOWN, EXPECTIN' TO SEE SOMETHIN' LIKE... LIKE JESUS LYIN' THERE.

BUT I JUST THOUGHT--BUGGER ME, WHAT AN UGLY LITTLE SOD. LOOKS LIKE A SHRIVELLED-UP OLD *MONKEY.*

'ERE--YOU CAN HOLD HER, IF YOU WANT.

ER... BETTER NOT. I'VE GOT ONE OF ME OWN ALREADY, LOVE--AND IT MIGHT GET JEALOUS.

WHAT...?

LOOK, I DON'T WANT TO BE RUDE, BUT I'M GOING TO PISS OFF. "HAPPY FAMILIES" STUFF JUST BRINGS OUT THE WORST IN ME.

THAT WAS YOUR PART OF THE DEAL, CHAS. I GOT MY OWN MONKEY TO HAUL AROUND--REMEMBER?

RIGHT, I'LL DRIVE YOU, MATE. WHERE D'YOU WANT TO GO?

CHAS...

NAH, IT'S ALL RIGHT--I COULD DO WITH A STROLL.

JUST DO US ONE SMALL FAVOR, EH?

ANYTHING, JOHN-- YOU KNOW YOU ONLY EVER HAVE TO ASK...

DON'T LET THEM CALL THE KID QUEENIE-- RIGHT?

The End

# YEARS GONE BY: A HELLBLAZER TIMELINE

## 1953
• John Constantine is born in Liverpool to Thomas and Mary Anne Constantine on May 10. During the birth, doctors discover a second child strangled in the womb. Mary Anne dies in labor. Thomas holds John responsible.

## 1961
• Thomas Constantine is sentenced to six months in prison for stealing women's underwear. John and Cheryl — his elder sister by seven years — are sent to stay with Thomas's sister Dolly and her husband Harry in Northampton.
• Playing in a disused quarry, John discovers what he believes to be a dead boy's heart. At first, John is entranced by its strange potential, before — in a moment of fear — he throws it away. Falling through the rusted tin roof of a small shed in the quarry, the heart possibly kills a tramp, who thus becomes one of the first casualties of John's magic.

## 1962
• Kit Ryan is born in Belfast to Paul and Concepta Ryan.

## 1963
• Papa Midnite kills his sister, Cedella, in Jamaica.

## 1967
• In one of his earliest acts of magic, John consigns his bad memories to a locket which he then buries in a time capsule. (The time capsule will be retrieved by Tim Hunter some 20 years later.)
• John is expelled from school. His relationship with his father at an all-time low, John curses Thomas to a slow death, but relents from actually killing him. (The curse will not be lifted until after his father's death in 1990).
• John runs away to London for the first time. Lives in Portobello, west London.

## 1968
• John becomes involved in a disastrous attempt to free Morpheus the Sandman from his imprisonment in Wych Cross by Magpie, one of the Dream King's servants.
• Caught by police, the runaway John is sent back home to Liverpool.

## 1969
• John runs away from home again. While hitchhiking to London, he is almost molested by Phillip Tolly, a priest driven insane by the First of the Fallen.
• Arriving at last in London, John moves in with Chas and his mother, Queenie.
• Over the next few years, John devotes himself to studying numerous forms of magic, gathering around him a group of similarly nascent magicians.

## 1977
• After seeing the Sex Pistols at the opening of London's Roxy Club, John forms his own band, Mucous Membrane, along with old school friend Gary Lester. They play their first gig at the Casanova Club in Newcastle.

## 1978
• Mucous Membrane releases its only single, "Venus of the Hardsell."
• While gigging at the Electric Banana club in Camden, north London, John meets Rich Eldridge, lead singer with punk band Fatal Gift.
• John's niece Gemma is born to Cheryl and her husband, Tony Masters.
• In the course of performing an exorcism at the Casanova Club in Newcastle, John summons a demon without knowing its true name (Nergal) and, unable to control it, he winds up inadvertently consigning the soul of an innocent child named Astra Logue to Hell. Driven half-mad by the experience, John is incarcerated in the "Ravenscar Secure Facility for the Dangerously Deranged," where he intermittently spends the next two years.

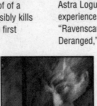

## 1979
• During a period away from the confines of Ravenscar, John is caught up in a temporal regression with Shade, The Changing Man, and they travel back to the Salem witch trials in seventeenth-century America.

## 1980
• Released from Ravenscar for the last time, John is blackmailed into resurrecting the recently deceased son of East End crime boss Harry Cooper. With help from Brendan and other friends the Reverend Rick Neilsen and Header, John summons a demon and binds it in the child's body.
• John meets Kit Ryan in Dublin through his friend Brendan Finn.

## 1983
• Along with Brendan, John steals the "Ace of Winchesters" — a gun with the ability to kill demons — from Papa Midnite for exotica collector Jerry O'Flynn.

## 1984
• After a botched attempt to exorcise two Victorian ghosts from the house of former Mucous Membrane drummer Beano, John is believed dead, and a funeral service is held in his memory. Of course, he turns up just as the ceremony is finishing, alive and well.
• The angel Tali and his pregnant demoness lover, Elle, ask John for refuge, but the offspring is taken by Archangels.

## 1985
• John meets the Swamp Thing for the first time in Louisiana as the Crisis on Infinite Earths reaches its devastating climax. John's girlfriend, Emma, is killed in New York by the Invunche — a servant of the Brujeria. A war with the Brujeria follows, which results in the deaths of Constantine's friends Ben Cox, Frank North, Judith and Anne-Marie.

## 1987
• Gary Lester — John's former band-mate in Mucous Membrane — is killed in New York by John and Papa Midnite.
• John encounters yuppie demons from Hell on the day of Prime Minister Margaret Thatcher's third election victory — June 11.

## 1988
• Gemma is kidnapped by an acolyte of the Damnation Army, but John and the mystic Zed rescue her.
• John becomes involved in the war between the Resurrection Crusade and the Damnation Army. Now leading the Damnation Army, John receives a transfusion of demon blood from Nergal. Wandering the streets of New York, driven to the edge of sanity by the demon blood, John contemplates suicide on his 35th birthday.
• The Swamp Thing appropriates John's body and uses it to conceive a child with his wife, Abby. She gives birth to a daughter whom they name Tefé.
• John at last learns Nergal's name. With help from Ritchie Simpson — the only other survivor of the Newcastle exorcism — John destroys Nergal but is subsequently forced to flee London, blamed for murders committed by the demon.
• On the run, John meets Marj and Merc and joins the Freedom Mob, settling down to a healthy outdoor existence. The peace is shattered when Merc is kidnapped by the sinister Masonic league controlling the Fear Machine.
• Finally free from Wych Cross, the Sandman searches for a pouch stolen during his captivity that contained the raw stuff of dreams. That search leads him to John Constantine, who bought the pouch some years earlier. It turns up in the hands of Rachel, an ex-girlfriend from his punk days, who has opened the pouch and become consumed by dreams. At Constantine's appeal, Morpheus gives Rachel a dream to take with her into death.
• The Fear Machine is broken by Zed, using ancient primal magic, with John and Marj's help.

## 1990
• John's father, Thomas, is brutally murdered by Sammy Morris, a serial killer known as the Family Man. Dragged into a cat-and-mouse game with the killer, John is complicit in Morris's eventual death.
• Gemma Masters suffers visions of her dead grandfather — trapped and unable to leave this plane — causing John to lift the curse he set on his father 23 years previously.
• Racked with remorse following his father's death, John turns to Marj and Merc for help. Merc forces John to confront his fears — en route, showing him a possible vision of his death — and helps him to unlock deeply suppressed truths about himself. John learns he killed his twin brother while still in the womb, and in an altered state of consciousness "meets" his alter ego and the two merge into one.
• Along with the Phantom Stranger, Doctor Occult and Mister E, John introduces Timothy Hunter to the world of magic.

## 1991

- John develops terminal lung cancer. Visiting Brendan Finn in the hope of finding a cure, John crosses the First of the Fallen.
- In a magnificent coup, John blackmails the ruling triumvirate of Hell into curing his cancer — but his long-term safety isn't guaranteed. The First swears revenge.
- John chances upon Kit in London, and the two become lovers.

## 1992

- John and psychic friend Nigel Archer fight Calibraxis, a blade demon who has possessed a member of the British Royal family. The demon is ultimately sent back to Hell.
- John cuts a sigil into the soul of Elle, protecting her from the First of the Fallen's wrath.
- Visiting Cheryl's family the week before Christmas, John finds that Gemma has been experimenting with magic.

## 1993

- John's 40th birthday party is attended by many of his extraordinary friends from down the years, including the Swamp Thing, the Phantom Stranger, Zatanna, the Lord of the Dance, and Elle.
- As part of ongoing preparations instigated by John to meet any threat posed by the First, Elle seduces the Archangel Gabriel and removes his heart.
- Kit is nearly killed when John unintentionally involves her in a dangerous feud with a racist organization. Kit leaves John, inducing a downward spiral that leaves him homeless and destitute on the streets of London. There, he faces the King of the Vampires — who had killed John's grandfather, William, during World War One — and destroys him.

## 1994

- Shortly after New Year's Day, a strange encounter with a dead World War Two fighter pilot helps John to get his life back on track.
- John travels to New York for a final, surreal encounter with Papa Midnite that sees him temporarily relegated to a piece of Hell populated by the souls of those destroyed by the American dream.
- The First of the Fallen begins his revenge against John, slowly murdering his closest friends — Header, Rick and Nige — and laying waste to Constantine's own plans for survival. But John pulls an ace from his sleeve and, with Elle's help, seemingly destroys the Devil.

## 1995

- John travels first to Philadelphia then Australia to investigate a supernatural virus that is causing the decay of reality.
- While in Australia, John enters the Aboriginal dreamtime and learns the power of mythotemic magic — adding to his portfolio.
- Returning to London, John is reunited with Rich Eldridge and his girlfriend Michelle and Jon Syder. Syder becomes possessed by Buer, who intends to restore the First of the Fallen to his former status. To free Syder, John must sign over part of his soul to Hell. As a result, though Syder — and also Astra — are released, the First of the Fallen is reinstated as ruler of Hell.

## 1996

- Recovering from his latest skirmish, John wanders into the woods and encounters a mysterious stranger who teaches him to face his own fears.
- Traveling to Hell, John meets his father Thomas, and learns that Thomas was responsible for the death of John's mother, thus damning him for eternity.
- John meets Dani Wright, an American journalist who becomes the new love interest in his life.

## 1997

- Becoming involved with Britain's mythical past, John learns that Rich is descended from King Arthur and battles to stop Myrrdin (otherwise known as the wizard Merlin) from finding the Holy Grail.
- Tim Hunter discovers a time capsule buried by Constantine some 30 years earlier within which he had banished his boyhood memories.
- John and Dani travel to New York to spend Thanksgiving with Dani's family. The First crashes the party, turning Dani's family against one another.

## 1998

- Seeking revenge against Constantine for betraying him during his war against the First of the Fallen, Elle hatches a plot to turn all of John's friends against him before moving in for the kill. To ensure the safety of everyone close to him, John must look for help from an unlikely source — the First of the Fallen — and sell his soul in the process.

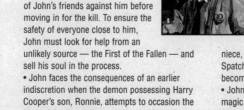

- John faces the consequences of an earlier indiscretion when the demon possessing Harry Cooper's son, Ronnie, attempts to occasion the birth of the Antichrist.

## 1999

- John and the Trenchcoat Brigade travel back in time to the Ukraine, 1648, where Constantine meets a distant relative — Pyotr Konstantin.
- John learns that an ex-girlfriend — Isabel — has been murdered by a rival magician and sets about exacting brutal vengeance.

## 2000

- John is sentenced to 35 years in a maximum security prison when he's framed for the murder of his longtime friend Richard "Lucky" Fermin. Employing his con-man skills and a dose of black magic, he quickly climbs the ranks to become the joint's top dog. After a full-scale riot plunges the prison into total chaos, John accepts the immunity offered to him by FBI Agent Frank Turro and embarks on a journey through the seedy underbelly of America in the hope of finding peace with Lucky's death.
- Soon thereafter, Constantine lands in Doglick, West Virginia. Attempting to atone for Lucky's demise, John instead finds himself contending with Lucky's two disgruntled brothers, a bestiality video ring and a demonic wild boar.

## 2001

- Stuck in a blizzard in the middle of nowhere, Constantine becomes a key player in a murder mystery that may or may not involve an urban legend known as the Iceman.
- John travels to the Pacific Northwest and comes face-to-face with Marjorie, Lucky's widow. He also discovers that Marjorie has found comfort in a white supremacy group which uses the Bible to support its hateful beliefs. In the end, John single-handedly dismantles the group, and his desire for atonement quickly vanishes when he learns that the famous multimillionaire S.W. Manor paid Marjorie for Lucky to commit suicide — and to frame Constantine for it.

## 2002

- With revenge in mind, Constantine agrees to work with Agent Turro to bring S.W. Manor to justice. Infiltrating the underground bondage club that the masochistic Manor frequents, John seduces him and shows him a vision of his long-dead parents — whose shame and horror at what he has become nearly drives him mad. After being goaded by John, Manor is tricked into thinking that he has killed Constantine, and he kills Agent Turro just before committing suicide.

## 2003

- John makes his way back to his hometown of Liverpool, only to learn that all of his friends and family think he perished in the prison riot. He makes peace with his estranged sister, Cheryl, and learns that his niece, Gemma, is missing. He also meets Angie Spatchcock, an aspiring magic user, who becomes his new love interest.
- John learns that Gemma has been learning magic in London from a certain Domine Fredericks. Blinded by her desire to become a magician on par with her beloved uncle, Gemma unwittingly becomes a pawn in Fredericks's plan to possess the Red Sepulchre, a magical weapon that only Constantine can identify. John turns the tables on Fredericks, using the Sepulchre to kill him, but Fredericks turns out to have been only part of a much grander, and far more deadly, design — one that threatens to destroy all of humanity.

## 2004

- After assembling a coalition of occultists to stave off the approaching Armageddon, John is tricked into releasing it instead, and mass death and insanity sweep across the globe. With help from Gemma, Angie, Chas and Swamp Thing, Constantine manages to snatch victory from the jaws of defeat once more — but the effort costs him his memory, and with it his identity.
- Wandering through the aftermath of the aborted apocalypse, John is targeted by a shape-shifting demon named Rosacarnis, who offers him a deal: his memories of the past in exchange for one day in her service. Seeing no other options, John accepts. In that single day, Constantine lives 40 years and fathers three demon children — Adam, Maria and Saul — bred by Rosacarnis to be his ultimate downfall.
- The story of John Constantine, Hellblazer, continues...

# JOHN CONSTANTINE'S LONDON

"... My name's John Constantine, and here I stay: haunted by London. And London, haunted by me..."

The history of London is rich in magic and mystery — from the attempts by Elizabethan court astrologer and mathematician John Dee to summon angels in his Clerkenwell home, to Jack the Ripper's bloody reign of terror on the streets of Whitechapel in the 19th century. It's only fitting that London has provided the backdrop for many of John Constantine's magical exploits — and so here we present a guide to some of the locations where he has faced down angels, demons and madmen.

• Shortly after John became involved with Kit Ryan, he received a particularly gruesome invitation to meet the King of the Vampires on HAMPSTEAD HEATH. Surrounded by a ghastly coterie of freaks and demons, the King of the Vampires tempted Constantine, appealing to his vanity in a bid to engage him as a spy — even offering him the chance to become a vampire. But Constantine rejected the offer, and the King of the Vampires promised to make him pay for his mistake. The opportunity arose when he stumbled across Constantine, living rough on the streets of London following his harrowing breakup with Kit Ryan. After much taunting, the King of the Vampires made to kill Constantine, but he developed an allergic reaction to the demon blood in Constantine's veins, and Constantine was able to seize the advantage, dragging the King of the Vampires into the sunlight where he spontaneously combusted.

• CAMDEN has been a consistent geographical landmark in Constantine's London: In 1977, riding the crest of the punk explosion, John formed his own band, Mucous Membrane. Gigging regularly at the Electric Banana — one of the least salubrious of Camden's many music venues — Constantine eventually made friends with Rich Eldridge, singer with another punk band, Fatal Gift... In the late seventies, John met Ray Monde, a camp homosexual who ran a clipping agency from the Camden curio shop Serendipity, and who became one of John's first friends in London. When Ray helped John hide his lover, the budding mystic Zed, from the Resurrection Crusaders, he was savagely beaten to death by Crusaders as punishment... In 1991, having returned to London, John had his fateful chance encounter with Kit Ryan, and the two became lovers... And in 1991, John came to the aid of the deceased proprietors of a local pub, Laura and Freddie Collins. When an unscrupulous property developer burned down the pub, Freddie's ghost wreaked violent retribution on those responsible, until John persuaded them to take a peaceful rest.

• For several years in the late eighties, John lived in a house in PADDINGTON that he shared with its owner, the ever-complaining Mrs. McGuire and a Rastafarian called Mighty Mouse. It was here that John encountered some of his most formidable demonic foes. Returning from his clash with the Brujeria, John discovered his old friend, Gary Lester, holed up in his toilet after exposure to the power of the demon Mnemoth. On another occasion, John was horrified to discover that the demon Nergal, seeking vengeance against Constantine for his hand in the defeat of the Damnation Army, had laid waste to the house and violently butchered Mrs. McGuire and Mighty Mouse. John returned to the house in 1991 to find it had remained derelict since Nergal had committed his earlier atrocities. It was there that Constantine, riddled with cancer and facing the wrath of the First of the Fallen, sold his soul to the Second and Third lords of Hell, creating a stalemate among the triumvirate that ensured they returned him to full health.

• Running away from home for the first time in 1967, John settled in the fashionable bohemian enclave of PORTOBELLO, near Notting Hill in west London. There he shared a house with a number of like-minded souls — Estella, Ravi, Pamela and Terry — passing time while practicing magic and getting stoned. A trip to Wych Cross in 1968, along with a young runaway named Oliver and Pamela's boyfriend Ivan, ended with disaster when Constantine and his new friends accidentally became involved in an attempt to free the Morpheus the Sandman from captivity. The experience had a profound effect on everyone, leaving Pamela in a coma from which she would never fully recover, and the crew parted ways soon after. Constantine was picked up by police and sent back to Liverpool.

• After returning from Australia in 1995, Constantine met up again with Rich and his girlfriend Michelle in TOOTING, south London (not shown). It was here that Constantine

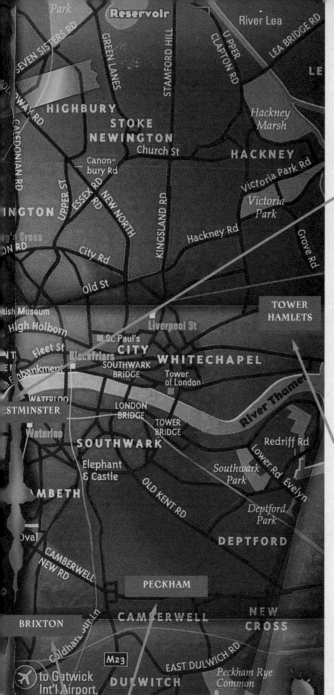

Constantine obtained a gun through Chas for protection. Constantine and the Family Man stalked one another through waste ground near Peckham Rye, before leaving London for a fatal confrontation near Liverpool.

• The central focus of power in Great Britain lies at WESTMINSTER, home to the Houses of Parliament and a number of exclusive private clubs — though none quite as select as the Caligula Club, where the powerful purge themselves of their most perverse whims, from sordid sex practices to murder. It was here that Government fixer Sir Peter Marston in 1992 bound the blade demon Calibraxis inside a member of the Royal Family, intending to watch the demon ascend the throne and England, subsequently, became the most powerful country in the world. But Calibraxis turned out to be the same demon who had possessed Jack the Ripper, and it embarked on a violent killing spree around London, forcing Marston to call on Constantine for help. Aided by Nige Archer, Constantine outfoxed Calibraxis and sent the demon back to Hell — with Marston in tow.

• One of London's most notorious housing estates, TOWER HAMLETS, in east London, has a long history of racial unrest. In 1994, it became the center of a race riot against which the First of the Fallen exacted his revenge on Constantine. Tensions already simmering following the murder of a black youth, Desmond Ridley, by a far-right racist movement reached boiling point when two police officers attempted to arrest Desmond's brother, George, on trumped-up charges, and their mother, Mrs. Ridley, was pushed down a flight of stairs to her death. An enraged George shot one of the police-men, the riot squad moved in, and Tower Hamlets erupted into violence. With 40 lying dead and chaos everywhere, Constantine plunged into the thick of it — only to find his friend Nige Archer dead at the hands of the First of the Fallen. The riot raged for two days before finally petering out, leaving George, rather like Constantine, to mourn the death of all his friends.

• Historically mired in violence through the gangland wars of the Krays and the Richardsons in the 1950s and '60s, DOCKLANDS, east London (not shown) has also been home to other, more unnatural mob dynas-ties, notably the Coopers, whom Constantine has had the misfortune to encounter on two occasions. In 1980, recently released from Ravenscar, John was coerced into resurrecting Harry Cooper's dead son, Ronnie, but instead bound a demon into the child's body. This botch would come back to haunt Constantine some 20 years later, when the demonic Ronnie would attempt to lay a blood-red carpet for the Antichrist gestating inside his poor father. Fortunately, Constantine and Chas were able to outsmart Ronnie and destroy the child just shortly after its birth.

was called upon to exorcise the spirit of a maltreated dog, help reunite the ghost of a dead soldier with his former love, and face the demon Havoc — soaking up the spectators' aggression at a soccer match in the nearby Selhurst Park grounds.

The multiracial south London suburb of BRIXTON was the site of the brutal occult murder of Constantine's former girlfriend Isabel Bracknell by Joshua Wright, a sadistic magician who had turned the young woman into a vessel for sex magic — a "scarlet woman" — before brutally murdering her. Attempting to lay Isabel's ghost to rest, Constantine, with the aid of a bent police officer named Watford, tracked down Wright and administered his own brand of jus-tice, leaving Wright an insane, beaten wreck.

Lying low after a chance encounter with the serial killer known as the Family Man in 1990, Constantine stayed above a betting shop where Chas worked in PECKHAM, south London. It was here that John learned that his father, Thomas, had been murdered by the Family Man — who had traveled to Peckham intending to kill John as well. Leaving a bloody swath in his wake, the Family Man put Constantine in fear for his life — so much so that

# THE HELLBLAZER LIBRARY

Where horror, dark magic,
and bad luck meet,
John Constantine is never far away.

**ORIGINAL SINS**
JAMIE DELANO/VARIOUS

**DANGEROUS HABITS**
GARTH ENNIS/VARIOUS

**FEAR AND LOATHING**
GARTH ENNIS/STEVE DILLON

**TAINTED LOVE**
GARTH ENNIS/STEVE DILLON

**DAMNATION'S FLAME**
GARTH ENNIS/STEVE DILLON/
WILLIAM SIMPSON/PETER SNEJBJERG

**RAKE AT THE GATES OF HELL**
GARTH ENNIS/STEVE DILLON

**SON OF MAN**
GARTH ENNIS/JOHN HIGGINS

**HAUNTED**
WARREN ELLIS/JOHN HIGGINS

**SETTING SUN**
WARREN ELLIS/VARIOUS

**HARD TIME**
BRIAN AZZARELLO/RICHARD CORBEN

**GOOD INTENTIONS**
BRIAN AZZARELLO/MARCELO FRUSIN

**FREEZES OVER**
BRIAN AZZARELLO/MARCELO FRUSIN/
GUY DAVIS/STEVE DILLON

**HIGHWATER**
BRIAN AZZARELLO/MARCELO FRUSIN/
GIUSEPPE CAMUNCOLI/CAMERON STEWART

**ALL HIS ENGINES**
MIKE CAREY/LEONARDO MANCO